SPRING 2015 NEW TITLES

Agota Kristof, *2 Novels:*
The Proof, The Third Lie
ISBN 978-1-909585-04-1; £8.99

Paulette Jonguitud, *Mildew*
ISBN 978-1-909585-03-4; £8.99

Matthew Siegel, *Blood Work*
ISBN 978-1-909585-05-8; £8.99

(B *editions*

www.cbeditions.com

Poetry Apollinaire · Fergus Allen · Alba Arikha · Beverley
Bie Brahic · Andrew Elliott · Nancy Gaffield · Joaquín Giannuzzi ·
Stephen Knight · J. O. Morgan · D. Nurkse · Dan O'Brien ·
Francis Ponge

Fiction Jonathan Barrow · Andrzej Bursa · Will Eaves ·
Stefan Grabinski · Gabriel Josipovici · Agota Kristof ·
Todd McEwen · David Markson · Miha Mazzini · Nicky Singer ·
May-Lan Tan · Dai Vaughan

'exceedingly classy' – Patricia Duncker
'wonderfully eclectic, quietly iconoclastic' – Mike Loveday
'admirably wayward' – Jeremy Noel-Tod

Trade orders: Central Books   *free UK delivery for website orders*
Representation: Inpress Books

Sonofabook 1   edited by Charles Boyle

Spring 2015

Cover: photo by Frantisek Seidel, c.1951, © Ceskokrumovský rozvojový fond spol. s.r.o., courtesy Museum Fotoatelier Seidel, Cesky Krumlov, Czech Republic.

Sonofabook is published by CB editions, 146 Percy Road, London W12 9QL. The contents of each issue are selected by a different editor. Copyright in each contribution remains with the author. To subscribe, see www.cbeditions.com. Advertising and submissions inquiries: info@cbeditions.com. Distributed by Central Books; represented by Inpress Books. CB editions acknowledges the financial assistance of Arts Council England in the publication of this magazine. Printed in England by T. J. International, Padstow, Cornwall. ISBN 978-1-909585-07-2.

Supported using public funding by **ARTS COUNCIL ENGLAND**   LOTTERY FUNDED

Preamble

CB editions started in 2007. Last year I scratched a seven-year itch and the result (after washing my hands) is *Sonofabook*. Each issue of this twice-yearly magazine will print generous selections of work by a small number of contributors, and will be edited by an invited writer, editor, critic, bookseller . . . The balance of fiction, non-fiction, poetry and work in translation will vary; one or other of these categories may take a holiday; but common to all the editors will be an interest in the kind of writing that tends to find its home on the lists of the smaller publishers rather than the more risk-averse mainstream ones. Issue 2 will be edited by Nicholas Lezard, writer and *Guardian* reviewer; issue 3 will be edited by Sophie Lewis, translator and editor-at-large with And Other Stories.

The present issue contains only new (or previously untranslated) work by writers closely associated with CB editions. Among the CBe authors *not* included here are Apollinaire, Andrzej Bursa, Joaquín Giannuzzi, Gert Hofmann, Gabriel Josipovici, Todd McEwen, David Markson, Miha Mazzini, Christopher Reid and others. Publishing this range of writers, in an economic climate that suggests this is a foolish thing to be doing, has been a privilege.

A word on independent bookshops, whose quarter-page adverts in this issue were offered free. Without good small bookshops it is very hard for small publishers to get their books out into the physical world. In February 2014 the Booksellers Association reported that the number of independent bookshops in the UK had fallen below 1,000, following a year-on-year decline over the previous decade. This massacre is in part the consequence of ebooks and online buying, but a key moment was the abolition of the Net Book Agreement in 1997. The ending of the NBA – which required retailers to sell books at the cover price – led to aggressive discounting (which actually forces *up* the cover price of books, as publishers struggle to maintain their margins); concentrated bookselling in the hands of chainstores, supermarkets and Amazon; and forced the closure of hundreds of bookshops. The literary culture of the UK was changed overnight; but while France and Germany legislate to restrict discounting and offer good breaks to independent bookshops, none of the political parties in the UK cares a damn, this not being a vote-winning issue.

Back when CBe started up, I put books in a bag and trekked around some of the independent bookshops in London. It rained. I had no distributor, no trade reps, no reviews, no credibility and no umbrella. Johnny de Falbe at Sandoe's read one of the books overnight and rang next day to order 40 copies; also supportive were Max Porter at Daunts (now an editor at Granta) and Matthew Crockatt at Crockatt & Powell (now with And Other Stories); and then Dennis Harrison at Albion Beatnik and Gavin Housley at Foyles and Jonathan Main at Bookseller Crow and Muna Khogali at Book & Kitchen, and others. I had never met any of these people before wandering into their shops. I owe them. The ads for bookshops in this first issue, and I hope in future issues too, are intended as more than just fillers.

ookSonofabookSonofabookSonofabookSonofabookSonofa
ofabookSonofabookSonofabookSonofabookSonofabookS
nofabook**Sonofabook**SonofabookSonofabookSonofaboo
SonofabookSonofabookSonofabookSonofabookSonofab
ookSonofabookSonofabookSono kSonofa
ofabookSonofabookSonofabook subscribe fabookS
nofabookSonofabookSonofabo www.cbeditions.com ofaboo
ookSonofabookSonofabookSonofabookSonofabookSonofa
ofabookSonofabookSonofabookSonofabookSonofabookS
nofabookSonofabookSonofabookSonofabookSonofaboo

ELIZABETH MIKESCH & MAY-LAN TAN

Five Motets

Ritual

One time, something grew inside me I couldn't tell anyone. When unconfident comperes explained away their tendons or perspex, all I felt was my skirts. All I felt was this citrusish itch tiding. I let my tongue laze out. I took a tweezer to stiffies. I stifled my digestif diamonds. I grazed on patent slime.

Everyone was asked was I Arabic. Everyone wasn't ruined yet. Everyone asked me how old I'd be. Everyone could smell besides me. Everyone knew how to cut meat. Everyone was interested in a contortionist. Everyone had tentative plans. Everyone went to checkups and asked after gourmet ketchups. Everyone had photo albums of only their face making faces. Everyone was sitting in a circle pulling oil. Everyone was craving miniature. Everyone was teaching themselves to streak or tanning ice floes. Everyone was spacing out and phoning up for capitals and putting it all on the tab. Everyone had cramps.

I had only mystical experiences with deer and the woods. I lived in a world without lube. I teemed with lunatic bacterium. I renamed them daily. They were staticky and knotted my hair, and they made me a homeopath. There is no such thing as sleep when they reign. I solely drank packets mixed with gathered water I branded and collected in a brownie pan. Warbling made my pains shine through my veins. Prehistoric turds get sold in the first store I see where I am trying to find minerals to salve me. You pay by gram.

The city starked me with its pleasure tariff, so I stapled my forelocks and taped my patient tits together. I craned by the fountain, swallowing curses. That summer, no one knew how to kneel. No one felt like stroking sides in the orchestra pit. No one talked about getting the gold flake. No one double-fisted buffet trays. No one remembered to stretch. No one was so into sketching the breakers. No one wanted to lick the beaters or bang up the shooters. No one did anything ever that summer except to turn up the gamma and await scabs.

Me, I belonged back there. I crushed pebbles to shred whiteheads from the sweat. I stabbed a swan, wore a mask made of picnics I watched from a hiding spot. I masturbated in fairy graveyards cutesy groups implanted. My cunt drooled all over a tarp I laid from abandoned flannels.

When it rained, I changed tense and make a friend finally.

Has anyone ever been buried in you? she asks.
Do you like head rubs?
Do you scare the air with your sads?
Do you plunk when you land?
Can you stink?
Are you plump?
I want to be an unmanicured garden of snake eggs and allergens.
A bed growing girls.
Have you mopped a floor with puke upon it fast?
To be sucked through a tube is a rare kind of honesty.
I love the buzz in your vulva when you can't keep yourself down.
I hate any question that isn't about nervous breakdowns.
I hope to be ordered in restaurants.
Over easy. Hold the me.
I can't hear another deer die at a glib intersection.
I want to be hospitalized because of fumes.
My heart is a hedgehog.
There are bugs in my lunchbox.

I wish to be the trampled cheeks of hotel pillows.
These are sliders of eyelet made up on plates of the aged.

We walked so far downhill, our pelvises were cops. We were holding each other's stays the whole time, but my cunt needed to feel the water that had always been there. I had to get wet up to my hipbones or I wouldn't know how to stop being hateful. Slander coursed through me. My friend knew. We were wearing dresses we found in the fog that fit wrong. We felt sowed. It was a day where you knew you wouldn't see the moon.

I never rap fast enough. I want to be prescribed. I can't go inside any building not made of beaded bones. I got tested by a mister who stains saints. He chased me through airports and stole me how to squeeze. When we got there, my pits smelled like the sky. We found it. When I broke, I felt it in my face.

Batgirl

There's a movie of me where I talk in a deep voice. I'm rich, and I have flashback parents. I'm fucking a new guy every time. He's daintily capable, and I'm distant. I'm saving him from danger. I last two and a half hours. People line up to watch. Some that come are dragged. Some wait until the cheap show a few weeks in the future. They wear booby-traps and Halloween costumes. They swing sideways.

It's all because I don't want bad things to go on downtown. Everything is dark, molded like nasty hair catchers in drains. I have to fly away to train in Nepal. Someone throws me in a pit, and I get so skinny. It gives me powers.

A lot of times, there are soliloquies about my destiny. The battle is just kind of on the schedule or part of the series. Saying anything aloud sounds stupid, so I'll scowl. My personal assistant prepped me weapons in case something happens.

My mouth sometimes looks like somebody else's mouth or one that's upside down, and the words can't touch. My confidante's a question mark. She doesn't always feel like it. She's an immigrant child with zeros for eyes and a nasal laser ray. We screw in a lightbulb scoffing thought bubbles for breakfast. We do masks together and fall off planes. She's Catholic, and I'm stabbing her in the waist a lot. We've been put here to stop our coworkers necking, but we don't do anything with them. We'd rather broil someone for saying pow.

I wear my long hair over my real hair. My tearaway pants are from my to-be-slit skirt. I'm endearing, moved by token mentored orphans I school and house. Whenever I'm not in the movie, my skin gets poxed in black dots. I always anodize in time. It runs off rayon. There's so much I have to tell you, but I can't open my mouth right now. I'm talking around the outside of the world blowing into a machine that knows me intimately. Routine locked me out. Or, as a rule, I like to lose keys. A locksmith ends me.

I won't tell you about pink chills in eras I've slept near. All you see is me in action. Ask me why I don't stay. You shouldn't be able to locate a person without fake trying a few planets.

Trilogy is pedigree, but halcyon gets me more. My reflexes slicked down my tail when I went number one. This story is written in stalactites. Where snow blows up is a flotation device. Laughing, there's a camera and that makes people rentals.

Pay fees to see me nap, but I'll never look back. You storm them ever sweeter. You ward them sometimes blonder. You might whisper to me like I'm there in your summer, panting without sound.

Darling Contessa

I happen to be a midnight booboo kisser, a squealer scourer. I won't steal anything that hasn't come out of Hello Kitty's head. Bionic Voodoo Contessa, have you ever been elected to tend a concession stand? Mother superiors blot the lilac grease of the for-sale pizzas as if it were your grease on purpose. Host mothers and hammerhead aunts get upset when their daughters ask me for synastry reports, and I do cartwheels on their wedding dread. I want to make new friends, but I cannot type without looking at the swanky pucker of my navel. People want to dissociate their skin from my hinges.

I hear you, say they.

Back to booboos, I eschew their gray-blue fumes to be a bruise. You get fed this fodder that you're a faith healer and begin to feel endeavored. My friends are boozy types who need to be unpeeled. Let them flake. I fake how I understand.

My lip gets this one scuffed pore, and the people I make up ask when will I say how they feel about me. They ask, 'Do I miss you still?' Or, 'Will I tell you what you mean to me tonight or soon?'

How do the dead stay dead?

Now the Imbiber is standing in the doorway in his scruff, fronting and faux posing saying, 'I'm sorry I'm naked.' He's borrowing my phone because he dropped his in a farmer's market in the middle of the moan. Last night he got numbers from a girl, and now he's mad he won't get to press the buttons. He calls someone about getting another phone on my phone too near my ear, hangs up and tells me the whole conversation again. He walks away and stands in the doorway to say it.

On our days off in his truck, he takes me on boyhood tours and tells me he's got to stop being such a drinker, but he can't stop drowning altogether. It happens to be his job. He wants to know if he'd be good for a Libra. I read him what I feel, and he mopes. I call him Droopy. I try to show him the hot little house where I broke my first bone and sprained my cunt when I dropped splay off the monkey bars. They were so mango yellow I liked to chew on them. I open my mouth to say it, and he justifies wearing his hat to me when I hadn't asked.

I hold my pee, and it hurts me.

I ask him to the movies, but he won't go. We eat standing up in the kitchen. I go to the movies alone, but I leave after three minutes. The whole flick is about men on men, but it's no fun. I go to Mexican-town and eat tacos and worry. My crimped lashes clump. I pull them, blank out at the bar. A muscle car scrapes by spraying a song something teevee.

My stepsister came to our sofa with her Sun-In and Red Hots. She smacked her lips and showed me how to strip. I have slippery hips, but I don't legato. All her scratch and sniff stickers smelled of Snickers and pepper.

When our parents broke up, we were holding our breath. Her father whorled her out and the smuck of blue made her body stream like she was melting back into the pool. I stand by the piano and start pocketing olives. All the walls are velvet art of my friends nude and glum. The bartender brings me a fizzless jacuzzi with a man floating facedown wearing a Swatch. I lick my straw and blow bubbles.

The barman's badhanded. His nachos grieve me. I like them with pica. He microwaved them into moles. I look into his chipped eyes and see French kisses frying in their beds. I picture proud swarms of mouths forced to laugh by skullbulbs and a man's hands palpating the laughter. The bartender says the show's dad is dead. I prick him with a paper umbrella and run into my rival.

In bed, I smudge my cunt smell like smoke all over my blankets. The graffiti out the window blathers: I dream of all the garbage on earth. Don't you want to be in cocktail clothes waving to the ocean? I always bullet trains to the last lines of gut-sick songs, trying to turn my meat into a melody of coney dogs.

Get into it, said anyone. They've never split a jacuzzi with me.
Prove it, said any actress.
Die off.

Did you ever try to grow yourself from sand, to tongue a clam and wear the beach like a clog? Wait until a blue boy washes up on your porch and fall in love with his backstroke. His spinal necklace echoing your earrings. Someone strokes a tiki torch. Someone stretches skins on a cart with one smoking wheel. Someone squeegees a barbell. Someone believes in bikinis. Someone's packed carrots grow white blush.

Laundry workers found me rumpled on the Ferris wheel, my satchel puffed with crabapples, gunk. Every limb tagged with its milk names. A bird flew with food in its mouth while I had food in my mouth, and I wanted to shoot it down. I forgot to say I wore tights and didn't take them off, so the pantyhose were soused. I like to piss in live water, even if it's a puddle where petals blow.

Listen, said the mouth.

I call the only one who understands, the bad man. I list my hubbubs, my dervishes. I tell him all the places I've been peppy and careened with stubbled bellhops. His peppermint cracks. His silence necks me with its sexless tines. I owe him you.

We share a beat when I fray my feet in the sink. He spits on the counter and we look for too long. He named his night for me. Touches my eyes for me. I feel signed.

Eurostar

My dad drove black Hummers. My mother was powder. They chris-
tened my brother Export. We were always a tassel bi. The summer we
all stopped being young, Dad shat his last diatribe. He died contrite
of success failure. He thought he was going to be something louder
than his loss. The family watched him float up through the sunroof.
His crotch flowered like agave.

I strung the greens of babyhood and spilled their sticky blush. Began
my gingham life stoned on Cheeto musk. The sofa ennobled me. I
learned the word proletariat over my bed. Magnets pricked my spine.
I adopted a posture like poplars.

A best friend was an origami papercut who lived on a hospital corner,
naming pain. Wearing lollipop rings and taping torch songs to a crush
who touched us. We shoplifted shao mai near the nuclear island. The
lanterns fished for blackened forks.

Buttons grew all over our bodies. Zircon tuned our lobes.

We played faint in wreck rooms, braved sweats. We maimed their
throttles and they sprayed us with skate rays. When they let us out
of the holding gate, we ran back. I was a natural: diamantine, so I
bopped town with a swarm of cutters and limped to pin-up school.

There I loved a glazier. I blew a wearer of stranded sand. I dizzied a
faint of face sophomoric affluent ad man. I spayed a last gasp who was
blistering saddlesore. I creamed an acerbic stammerer who resented
my glamour.

Since they took away my stylus, my parting is my salvation. I can
still see through my mucky eye, so I blab about mastheads to a wan
actuary. I sharpen what I hatch and cower under awnings. When
I've showered enough, I plump for a mic I hold in my mouth like a

baby animal. I get so popular from having the best number of puncture wounds and doing something with frosting in a can that clicks. Everything is found beneath my bed when I barf.

My augur is flimflam until someone is out to get me. Know what I mean. Everyone decorates the phases of the moon like a second coming. If I exclaim to you how I got to be the bride of seiners, who cares. How many people do you know have documentaries made for them?

I leave the sea forever, and I say, Oh me, I choose to secrete sleepy black film. I try you between the eyes for quarter squint.

Name someone you know famished for tranquil screens, like the plants who lose leaves. Can you write a crop-strangled song that makes paint wet again? I'm allowed only two ugly things. They sawed ice under my tongue. I can look so soft with my mouth.

Glub Doesn't Get It

Glub got mean because she's gleam-eyed like the one who swanned in. Lycra holds her in the shape of a spoon. Glub has a thin twin whose name is nicer who wears posts is the one with the pricky pillow.

I camped out crisscross hiding from porno. Day-to-day was what I said. I heard herself say it through root vegetable cochleas. Let's sift through goobers in the lair of my purse shilled with MRSA, and spread it in whichever bed I wet. I was unkempt and bendered. This is when I lived in the stirrups part of a van. This is when I was hiding from a fan. I listened from the borrowed bed to the grackles while the people who showered spoke low of me aglow.

That was the most insidious part, said the acned tutor behooved. He had lost his ability to memorize whole plays and he was held together with snail sick. I played one day a week in a grey chair. What I did was look out at trees and prize my itchy thighs and commandeer commas while everyone talked in the loudest voice.

Glub swam and lit things on fire. She sometimes tried to film me through holes. The whole house congregated besides her and me on the sofa or the living room floor. I weaseled wines and healthful chips from her grips. Some radio station boss tossed me around for mispronouncing bun. I held on to it. Some man told me I could charm ham.

I was a beer pourer in a park where artificial ice killed all grass. I cried to taps. VIPs wanted the biggest curls. I panicked at a felon in a headband. The birds were air rats. The river was green. There were men in only overalls. There were women in pretzeled necklaces disrobing from glugging. I tried to imagine what type plant a peanut was and could not.

We ran out of beer. She told people it was my piss and charged treble. We ran out of things to say. I had eyeboogers, but I told people it was introversion. We ran out of tampons and pads. We stole our boyfriends' friends' cars. We took their wallets on trips to slime commissaries. We slung them over fences like toothy apothecaries. We Googled our doom and what came up was turducken.

Put stick-on earrings on all dick tips for seconds at a time. It's so decorative.

Glub sublets a blubber factory with two roofs where she lays out and makes out and sleeps for people. She looks like God's body. The silhouette is bent. It fattens her face. She traces herself in the shape of a shark. Dark marker stripes her. I rub her off, it off her. She writes me on the bridge. Hands are our style, and we take them to a metal show. I'm in the sky trying to milk someone when Glub says never be made afraid of what you've made so good. You know your time is flowers.

NANCY GAFFIELD

Springtime in the Rockies

Springtime in the Rockies *is a 1937 film starring Gene Autry based on the country song of the same title. It is also the title of a sequence of poems by Brian Marley. Ed Dorn also wrote a poem with this title.*

1/14

Climb down off the roof
my tongue. Happiness has to be
learned like long division.
The last supermoon dips
a toe in Brainerd Lake. Moose in slo-mo
racked & pinioned, rising out
of the willows. Pierce-arrow
screams from the trees. Sonofabitch.
Travelling through stretches of pine
forest fleshed out in undergrowth,
what the fire left behind
concertinaed charcoal husks.
Not so impressed with the trophy,
the dead glass eye, Eunice

2/14

goes instead to the drugstore
where Fritz fondles her between
the customers & closing time.
Give me that ole time religion.
Your sorrows pin you to
this place. You'll move to another city,
Eunice, but nothing is ever over.
One person's disaster is another's
Independence Day. It's hard to
anchor yourself when the water
keeps rising & re-drawing the borders.
The Poudre is a predicament
of uprooted limbs. This is not
the cool light of dawn but a shortcut

3/4

to hell on the I-25 bi-polar & fugue.
I wore my leather chaps on Coyote Ridge.
For fifteen years the Sleeping
Indian spread out
before me. Look – I said – I want
to see the sea plaintively dragging
its skirt of plankton over the knees
of the world. Chinooks part
the canopy & I catch a glimpse
of a half-moon marooned & pining
in the assarts. I am reduced to a
grub but you claim I saved
your life though probably it was more
a matter of being in the wrong place

4/14

at the right time the killer
carried a crossbow & the bull
never stood a chance. Tame as a
sitting duck in a willow copse.
He was no huntsman, this was no quarry.
He shot the arrow, the animal fled
though not too far, not so far
as the forest. He died in open field.
In the Airstream Eunice watches
Walter & Jesse on Blu-ray.
Losers get flushed down
the can & what remains
of a man is a red stain
over & under

5/14

I stole the title from Brian Marley.
Today is the 50th anniversary of the Pop
Tart. You make me feel so young.
Eunice prefers the country
song – tractors, trucks, fishing, beer
& Jesus, go figure. She was a runner
born for leaving. On the way through
town she spies with her little eye
her father's mortuary has been turned
into offices. A psychoanalyst occupies the old
embalming room & across the street the Waterloo
Bar & Grill where the cinema used
to be. Can't get back. Can't
get back, the train's

6/14

refrain. The moment flickers.
Eunice measures out her life
in beer mats. Feeling kind
of restless. The old cowboy bar
upside the railroad track is closed,
the bullet holes in the bar
visible through the window.
The coal miner's shack she grew up in
sold for half a million. On Mockingbird
Hill words rush by with plenty of
espace between & around.
Hello Hollo. Your ghost wanders
round these parts with intent
Coo COO coo COO

7/14

Beware of parataxis. The New Poets
(British Branch) want nothing
to do with you. Don't worry about
the asshole in the corner who thanks you
for not using the mike. I wish
life was an opera I could live
in with my little sweetheart
of the mountains. Get back to that simpler
time when dogs smiled at me
from the porch. We find ourselves
in the Rockies far away on November 2,
1972. Boulder sees first measurable snowfall
of the season, but sunny skies set to return.
Another year or forty pass & we're still

8/14

here. In Rocky Park they shoot moose
don't they? Wolves howl at sundown.
Make it legal it's not fun
any more. I move smoothly through
quandariness. Continental Drift on the shelf
next to Hejinian, Hilson, Hollo & Howe.
'Sheets clapped at sky' & it's wonderful
weather for drying but no one hangs
their laundry out any more. Thinking
is writing. The page is paved with
good intentions never really knowing
why the wheelbarrow's full of flint.
The bough quakes in anticipation
of winter smeared on thick

9/14

reactive. I am in a nomad
situation of craggy peaks
Continental Divide spruce
forest I-witnessing track &
call. This is crewel work.
Waadurrr cool & clear. Scissor-work.
Interaction with objects inside the event
horizon all paths lead to. He embroiders
the fir floor with garnets. White
mist low to the ground
I lay myself down
on the land. With the bones
of my ancestors. Different elements
are composed of air

10/14

thin like sentences on unbleached
muslin. Mother brought me up on
Spoon River. I could recite
Lucinda Matlock before I learned
my Catechism. Dear Ghost,
that was a simpler time before
my syntax went a-roaming.
Eunice can't remember the hand
that struck but the mark
is still there. Geography is a science
of trial & error but the Rockies
remain where they were planted
between us. Blue, brown & white
twitch & go

11/14

Grey geese fly overhead
in the letter V reversed. Swoosh
of wing beats
hush of home. Am pendulum
& composed of thirteen letters. The final
cluster is a clearing. An = one or none.
Across the sea I am not
one with my native land.
Am bivalent. Let's forget that
with a white sheet he tried
to erase me. With fire
he tried to deface me.
Put it to him later
He said 'can't remember'

12/14

the hot sun or the horizon
melting into liquid gold. Otherworld
flight of the black swift,
theorist of the wet cave she
compasses, spins, rolls &
banks. Pivot of quartzite walls
Uncompaghre waterfall.
'Go West young man
and grow up with the country.'
Meeker did & paved it
with his failures. They named
a town after him. Popular with hunters,
a favourite of prominent Americans,
a river runs through it

13/14

luminous certainty of the road
I sit on the shoulder. Double
Bind. Fearstorm & the sea
splintering. When Eunice was a child
she had a bear, named it Trauma.
In a green rectangular state
am suspended, am swinging
between selection & combination
or similarity & contiguity. Grammar
in locomotion, the whistle
of a freight train. Stepping
through the front door I
don't recognise anyone.
From now on life will unfold

14/14

in a topography of pain –
limestone, dolomite,
sandstone & shale. Laramide
Orogeny, thrust-faulting foothills
of rock under pressure. The continent
riding along on the wave
of convection, spreading across
the seafloor. On the corner of Walnut
& Main 'I bear the traces
impressed upon me.' Excessive light dispels
ghosts. Lived here once,
existing from the collar up,
the sleeves out. Poised between darkness
& face, a trick of light.

Notes

1/14
The Pierce arrow is also known as the
NOR operator in logic, as introduced by
Charles Sanders Pierce. The symbol is ↓.

2/14
'You'll move to another city, Eunice, but
nothing is ever over' from the 2013 TV
series *True Detective*.

3/14
People living along the Front Range urban corridor in Colorado call the higher
back range mountains (Mount Meeker
and Longs Peak) 'The Sleeping Indian.'

In the Assarts is the title of Jeff Hilson's

2010 collection of sonnets published by
Veer. Hilson provides a definition of the
word 'assarts' from the *OED* as 'A piece
of forest land converted into arable by
grubbing up the trees and brushwood;
a clearing in a forest.' See also Hilson's
Introduction to *The Reality Street Book
of Sonnets* (2008).

4/14
Walter and Jesse are characters in the
2013 American TV series *Breaking Bad*.

5/14
The title referred to is 'Springtime in the
Rockies'.

6/14

'Words rush by with plenty of espace between and around' is a borrowing from Anselm Hollo's poem 40 in *rue Wilson Monday*, La Almeda Press, 1988: 'how about just a few words / decoratively arranged on the page / with plenty of espace / between them around them . . .' Hollo taught at the Jack Kerouac School of Disembodied Poetics, Naropa University in Boulder. In 2001 poets and critics associated with SUNY Buffalo's Poetics Programme named Hollo 'anti-laureate' in protest against the appointment of Billy Collins as Poet Laureate Consultant in Poetry to the Library of Congress.

7/14

In Hollo's poem 15: 'give up your ampersands & lowercase "I"s / they still won't like you / the bosses of official verse culture / (U.S. branch)' – *rue Wilson Monday*.

The concept of parataxis refers to what Ron Silliman calls 'the new sentence' which disrupts the syllogistic force of the sentence by interrupting the logical chains from which arguments and propositions flow.

The 'New Poets' relates to the 20 poets selected by the Poetry Book Society in 2014 to be 'Britain's Next Generation of Poets'.

'my little sweetheart of the mountains' is a quotation from Autry's song.

8/14

'Make it legal and it's not fun any more' may refer to Colorado's recent legalisation of the sale and use of marijuana for recreational purposes.

The word 'quandariness' appears in the Frank O'Hara poem 'The Day Lady Died'.

Lyn Hejinian writes in *My Life* (2008): 'My Lives on a shelf by Trotsky, George Sand.'

'Sheets clapped at sky' is from Susan Howe's 1980 poem 'The Liberties'.

9/14

The term 'event horizon' refers to the boundary marking limits of a black hole. In popular usage, it may mean the point of no return.

10/14

Spoon River is a tributary of the Illinois River in west central Illinois. The poem 'Lucinda Matlock' appears in *Spoon River Anthology* (1915).

11/14

Susan Howe's poem 'The Liberties' (Section III) contains the following word puzzle:

I am composed of nine letters.
1 is the subject of a proposition in logic.
2 is a female sheep, or tree.
3 is equal to one.
4 is a beginning
5 & 7 are nothing
6, 7 & 8 are a question, or salutation.
6, 7, 8 & 9 are deep, a depression.

12/14

'Uncompaghre' refers to the Ute tribe of southern Colorado. Chief Ouray (Arrow) became chief of the Ute people and tried to negotiate a treaty with the US Government to retain their land.

'Go West young man and grow up with the country' was a statement attributed to Horace Greeley, though the origin of the phrase is uncertain. It relates to America's expansionist agenda popularised under the phrase 'Manifest Destiny'.

Nathan Meeker was the founder of Greeley, Colorado, a town situated slightly north-east of the Front Range urban corridor. In 1878 he was appointed Indian Agent in charge of the Ute Reservation. He was an authoritarian figure who tried to impose his religious beliefs on the tribe, as well as modern methods of farming and cattle raising. The Utes refused to give up their way of life, and when Meeker located his headquarters on land sacred to the Utes, Meeker was killed along with eleven other men by

a small band of warriors. His wife and daughter were taken captive but later released. Theodore Roosevelt, amongst others, is known to have hunted for mountain lions in the area.

14/14
Laramide Orogeny is the term used to describe the formation of the Rocky Mountains.

'I bear the traces impressed upon me' is a quotation from Anselm Hollo's poem 62 in *rue Wilson Monday*.

The idea that women live 'from the collar up, the sleeves out' comes from Junichiro Tanizaki's book *In Praise of Shadows*. The phrase refers to the 'erotic power' of the Noh actor, whose face, neck and hands are the only flesh visible.

WILL EAVES

The Miscreants

From a novel-in-progress, inspired by aspects of the life and work of Alan Turing.

It is always possible for the computer to break off from his work, to go away and forget all about it, and later to come back and go on with it. If he does this he must leave a note of instructions (written in some standard form) explaining how the work is to be continued.
– A. M. Turing, 'On Computable Numbers, with an Application to the *Entscheidungsproblem*'

Acoustic dark: voices and squeaks, the slide and shunt of forms. The darkness has a leathern softness, lit by brass flashes. The brightness of a buckle or the ring of metal round an inkwell permit me the briefest of glimpses of faces, shoes, socks, ties and desks – before I'm on the move again, on the back wall, rising through polished wood. Wainscotting. Painted initials, glorious lists scroll down before me. I'm behind the sad letters (Atkins, B. S., Atkins, J. T.), scanning from right to left until a sort of dawn breaks and I'm clear.

A boy with parted hair and brown unflinching eyes looks through me, through the pane: Alec Pryor, the name just visible in an upturned collar. Beside him sits a paler, neater blond boy, C. C. Molyneaux (according to a red notebook), fully absorbed in the lesson, unlike his friend, who yawns and mists the glass so that my view of both boys is obscured. When the mist clears, Pryor stares with a new intensity. He whispers 'Absolute . . .' and presses with his dirty shoe on the much cleaner toe of C.C.M. Turns back to face the front seconds before the master stops chalking equations on the board.

'Hindsight,' the master's high and drifting voice declares, 'may have a scientific use. Physical measurements that we make now, of particles in flight, affect the story we can tell about the past.'

The thirty lives in this cold room, seen from some distant vantage-point, are like the hopeful lanterns of a struggling ferry .

'That is the world of quantum measurement advanced by Mr Schrödinger. But note: the past itself is still secure. Pryor. I saw you roll your eyes. I heard you say "nonsense". These marks of insolence are fixed. While I may change the story that I tell of them, should any mitigating information come to light, I may not change the marks themselves. On a related matter, we may not go back. We recollect our own past and form impressions of history in general. But to revisit any part of it is out of the question, unless we are unhinged and can mistake the fact of being able to imagine Agincourt for Agincourt itself.'

'Sir.' The blond boy raises his hand only to lower it again. He has a way of interrupting and then hesitating that wrongfoots authority. Masters forget to chide or punish him. They like him. He has interesting things to say.

'Molyneaux.'

'What if you could really go there, sir, the past, I mean? Observing, not acting. But *be* there, knowing it, much more than if you were just looking back?'

'Charming hypothesis.' The master smiles. The other boys begin to yawn or look bemused. 'Alas, here we intrude upon the realm of fantasy.'

'You'd need a machine,' Pryor says, his shoe pressing on Molyneaux's.

'As I was saying, Pryor, here we part company with the real. If you could build such a machine, then Mr Wells and Mr Hilton, not to mention Mr Wilfrid Ashley of the Ministry of Transport, would be breaking down your door. Now –'

'But sir,' Pryor objects. He's come alive and speaks quickly. 'It only need be hypothetical. We only need to know what *sort* of machine it would be, for now. To have an abstract idea.'

He laughs softly. One dissipating 'ha!', the wheeze of a harmonica.

Seated, holding his chalk, the master says, 'Go on.'

It isn't what the boy says that matters. It is the boy himself, his shyness overcompensated for by chatter, dares and intellect.

Pryor explains. A group of individuals have an idea, work hard, give way to others, who refine the problem in a different way until it's solved or, probably, transformed. The abstraction evolves until it can be made. It takes a certain quantity of time. 'It's just an algorithm, sir. Like anything. Like any set of instructions. A time machine to build another time machine!

'And then, as well, of course' – it's strange the way his nerves produce a cry, as though he were wailing 'listen to me' – 'you don't *have* to build anything to time travel. If you are here, in Wargrave, and I'm far away –'

'How far?' says someone else.

'Oh, I don't know. Ten billion –'

'Ten billion!'

'– light years. And I am there, and I walk just a few steps on, away from you . . . well, doing that, I turn into your past. My "now"'is long before you're even born. Or if I walk *towards* the Earth, my now is your future, in which a time machine exists. In which we use them – well, sir, all the time. Quite commonly.'

Master and Molyneaux and twenty other pairs of eyes bend light towards the figure by the window, with its face half-cut by shadow and half blinking in the sun. It is a humorous face, eager. He looks so young, dark hair and brows, heavy as cornices, sharpened by sudden growth, the jacket on broad shoulders waiting to be filled. His lips are parted wide enough for me to see the hint of supernatural incision – small and backwards-sloping teeth.

'I'm very taken with that idea,' says Pryor, when the bell goes and the boys rise, muttering. 'Of *yours*,' he adds, his eyes still bright and anxiously moving, aware of Molyneaux's silence. 'Very taken. It's like telepathy. The silent understanding. And so Roman, the two-headed God –'

'Pryor.'

'Or like backstroke, you know. Facing backwards, going forwards – in a different element, and one you can't *fully* resist, so you're never *out* of the water. The thing I didn't like was Stallbrook's vagueness. "Particles in flight." What does that mean? They're not part of some other medium. He doesn't see, does he?'

'Pryor. Just –'

'What?'

'Be quiet.'

The boy is skewered. We're in a corridor where I can hear more than I see. Swaddled by wood, I sense his smiling injury. And Molyneaux, from whom a shape extends to merge with his friend's darker mass, relents. 'You're a good sort, Pryor. We talk a lot. You know so much about, well . . . iodates, for one thing. And the whole of Stinks.' The dark mass shifts, emits an aspirated 'ha!' 'Only, you oughtn't make the Colonel look small. He's on our side, and we've a lot to thank him for. And what,' his voice drops, 'was that business with the shoe about? No more of that. It's . . . excessive. There's a good chap.'

The pale form pulls free of its companion and leaves. Pryor walks slowly in the other direction, towards the common room and a pierglass.

Now, from the mirror, I can see him properly again. His chin-raised profile glides unreadably. He looks stoic. Around the corner, in the cloistered gallery, I lose clear sight of him. The wood absorbs a little heat. His thermal shape alters, its uprightness a shade reduced, as though his head were bowed. He seems to hug his books and several 'ha!'s escape, ash-white, embered, into the air.

More bells, more boys, blurred faces, voices and a tide of youth.

Pryor turns round and runs back down the corridor the way he came, his head held high. He's fast. I see him intermittently, as sharply as a passenger at night sees his reflection in the mirror of a train window. He comes and goes: field flashes of presence. The hair has fallen free, he scarcely seems to breathe, his books pinned to his chest, the right arm slicing air. Flushed now, he catches Molyneaux beside a pair of double doors. Through their portholes he sees a class changing, hanging up clothes on hooks, glockenspiel ribs, hands clasping cuffs, an air of general alarm. There's tiled noise. Others barge past. I can't hear what Pryor has said. His voice swings back and forth. His hand is briefly on his friend's shoulder but soon withdrawn, and now he holds the door.

Molyneaux smiles, looks pleased to have been caught. More like a friend than heretofore. Flattered, relieved. Hungry.

'I'm going tonight. Across the lake. It's fifty yards – sixty, no more.'

'And raspberries?'

'All kinds of fruit,' Pryor confirms. 'A feast.'

'What if you faint? It'll be cold.'

'I only faint at blood. That's perfectly normal.'

'I had to carry you last time.'

Pryor laughs silently, another little wolfish yawn. 'I know you did, but this won't be the same. It's not footer. As long as you don't cut yourself sculling. In any case, it'll be dark. Pitch black. I'd never see you bleed.'

'You are impossible.'

'A thing is impossible. I am *invisible*, I think you mean.'

But that is not entirely true. Invisibility, the plane of presence beyond sight, is very rare. What draws the eye, nocturnally, is what we know is there.

Later that night, a full moon sticks in the poplars above the shut boat-house, and by its light a heron stalks beyond the ramp, peers at the onyx lake water. Head feathers lifting from the neck give it the disapproving look of Colonel Stallbrook on the sidelines at a rout.

Pryor jiggles the boat-house lock. He can't force it. 'Nearly, nearly…' Molyneaux hugs himself, heron-like guardian of his friend and yet another failed scheme. 'It doesn't seem to want to go,' Pryor admits, standing. 'I'm sorry. Wrong damn pin.'

Despite the chill, Molyneaux grins. They pause to look at each other, the mad assortment of their clothes, pullovers, dressing gowns and plimsolls for rowing. Pryor dusts off his hands and sheds his outer layers, turns while removing vest and pants and walks down to the water's edge.

And in.

Amazed, Molyneaux stares. The water laps Pryor's luminous rear. An audible *fsss* and the naked boy's white bottom disappears, his arms surrendering. Molyneaux glances round. They haven't been followed. The heron's carved out of blue-grey; a little owl calls further off, perhaps as far away as Deauville, land of greenhouses and raspberry canes. Pryor bobs seal-like in the black expanse.

'Come in!' he whisper-shouts. 'We'll swim.'

Molyneaux balks. He's neither weak nor shy. He simply has foresight, a sense of what might come to pass. Compared to Pryor, he's less nervous and less apt to be reckless. He plans – his work is very neat – and that of course is what makes Alec, who is clumsy, his best friend. They are a pair. It's strange, he often thinks, that Pryor doesn't seem to have another friend. He could be popular enough. He has a wit. (He liked 'one line in *Hamlet*, and it is the last'.) He's strong – runs like the wind. Perhaps he simply doesn't care. He certainly gives everyone the cold shoulder. *Noli me tangere.* Everyone else, that is.

They swim across the lake that forms a natural boundary to Wargrave School, in search of food. They are the hunter-gatherers of a famished tribe, following a moonlit trail, suspended in a darkened element, wind-ruffled where the ox-bow widens and the river terrace drops. Halfway between the boathouse and the other shore, Pryor stops, treading water, waits for Molyneaux, who's making slow progress, breathing poorly, each stroke laboriously conceived.

Pryor prefers to swim beneath the surface of the lake, where he can go faster. He waits and hangs, expelling air so that he sinks, and while he sinks opens his eyes to watch the water's relic luminosity vanish. Into the dark he falls and feels almost no resistance, his weight distributed. 'I'm not falling,' he thinks. 'The earth rises.' He has no force. The massive body of the lake bottom – its feet of leaves and grit, the old floodplain, bedrock, downfold and crust, the whole planet – rushes to greet his cold body.

He has the feeling that he's staring back in time, or at another part of time. And, as he stares, the white, blown carcass of a moon-like fish – a tench – stares back from the reed-bed, its ripped flesh waving in a dense current.

On the far side of Deauville Lake, the Deauvilles, Ceylonese tea giants, built their summer house, and round it in a fertile half-acre they planted an orchard – apples, plums (espaliered), damsons, raspberry canes. It stretches down to shiny pebbles and a gravel-bed, in whose unkind embrace the two boys lie, shocked by exposure, both shaking. Molyneaux shakes a little less. His breath comes, when it comes at all, in whistles. He is curled up like a louse. On his blue chest, a salvage team hammers for scrap, battering lungs and heart.

'Alec –'

The other boy makes no reply, but picks his friend up and hauls him through dusty canes towards the summer house – a pavilion with rattan chairs, a day-bed, blankets in a pile. The French windows are locked. The waning gibbous moon behind Pryor is bright, and I can see his desperation at the pane – the pane that houses me. He shades his eyes to see inside. The body of Chris Molyneaux has one arm about Pryor's neck, one foot dragging, the other twisting free.

Panic distracts; it does not concentrate the mind and, while he casts about for stones, Pryor scents warlike omens in the air. A cat, loping along the blue shore-line, stops to observe the scene. A field-mouse trails from its mouth. There are others, among the trees. The secret population of the night, avid for death – and Pryor, unwilling to drop his friend, afraid to break the glass. What if he cuts his hand and faints? Who'll help them then?

Molyneaux's hanging arm swings once and – points.

A metal hint from underneath a grey stock brick. Pryor lays down the painful weight – Molyneaux twitches, tries to cough – and takes the key and thrusts it in the lock. Something has warped, worked loose; Molyneaux is lying at his feet in the spring mulch, leaves glossy-dark as patent shoes, his body thin and starved but smooth, like some young chief not yet committed to his passage grave, waiting for earth and chalk to wrap him round.

Inside the pavilion, above the day-bed glows a deer's skull. Pryor shivers. He didn't see it there before, although it's bright as Sirius in

Canis Major, Procyon, or Capella. And by an optical effect (the angle of the moon), his own reflection peers out from the animal's long head, which grunts and stares.

The animal he has become inspires him to charge. He butts the door. It falls open, a clatter of springs and uncorked wood. A lightning crack divides my pane and I see everything faulted and thrown.

Pryor lifts Molyneaux, somehow, on to the bed, though Pryor himself is exhausted. Molyneaux's quiet, his eyes fixed on the goal of survival. Their nakedness a fact, the boys seek warmth, a cave, some rest. The furnishings feel alien and obvious – three blankets with a herringbone pattern, the striped provisional mattress, cushions to make a body comfortable.

When he has put a chair against the door, Pryor climbs into bed and pulls the blankets round them both. Facing the wall and held, Christopher Molyneaux grows no colder. Nothing is said. No more is done. The armour of his chest unfastens in the presence of his friend, whose nervous heat is life.

'I'll give myself up,' Pryor says, eyes closed, at dawn. 'I'll go back in a minute. To fetch help. Don't worry, I'll say it was all my fault.'

The words are whispered into Molyneaux's white shoulder. Neither body moves. The lake has dried on them.

An hour later, Pryor wakes again and leaves the nest. Molyneaux stays, watching the paint acquire a faint colour.

Pryor unhooks the deer's skull from the wall above his still curled-up companion. Examines it. Not a good specimen – the back half of the lower jaw's missing, a gap that, with the open cranial cavity, makes room enough for Pryor's head.

He puts it on.

Molyneaux rolls over to see a creature in the doorway of the summerhouse. Behind it stirs the morning mist, to which the creature's breath patiently adds, and behind that a boat greeting the island's little stage – the stage the two boys missed last night.

Appalled voices. The creature flinches at the sound. Its stag-like head jerks five degrees, returns to gaze at Molyneaux as all around them trees explode with donnish crows and exclamations from the shore.

A step further inside the house. The creature bows its head to Molyneaux's shy hand, offers itself. Its skin is rough, a blanket-hide, its scent the tea of wintered leaves, its eyes deep-set and warm.

'And *she* was miles from anywhere in Indochina, in the hills. Not even *there...*'

The woman with the Colonel wears a matron's uniform. Their clothes, put on in haste, look tight, uncomfortable.

'Are these things yours?'

It's an irrelevant question, like asking 'and what sort of time do you call this?' Into the answering silence pours the questioner's self-doubt, his powerless pride. Stallbrook's mouth overworks, wet with dismay. He nods towards matron, who holds the dressing gowns and shoes. 'I know –' he starts. 'Good God, Pryor, this little escapade – have you no care? Did you not think what it might do? Your father, he and I . . . ought we to be ashamed of you?'

'Day he was born . . .' Matron whispers. (He has turned out exactly as she thought he would. Just look at him! See how the boy has wrapped himself in standard issue, like those poor souls in the newspaper! But he is touched, whatever Colonel Stallbrook says. Who could forget the way he came to Wargrave, on the first day of the General Strike, on foot, without a change of clothes? 'I am Pryor. I ran from Southampton.' And what is that the little monster has upon his head? Who does he think he is?)

'Who do you think you are?'

'*I am the Red Lady of Paveland.*'

'He has gone mad.'

'Put these back on at once.' Stallbrook advances, throws the dressing gowns and pullovers at Pryor's feet and points, enraged, at the wide door and cracked window. 'Trespass. Breaking and entering.' His arm outstretched, his brow sweating. 'You've no idea, the fix you're in.'

The adolescent shaman doesn't budge an inch. A stillness holds them all, a pause before the sun appears. Without a class of witnesses, without the rows of small believers with their small beliefs, the master and his pinafored attendant are like empty postboxes, waiting for purposes to visit them.

The other boy, Molyneaux, where is he? The thought occurs to Stallbrook as the morning sun strikes through the island's poplars, lights the raspberry canes and apple trees, the Bath stone of the squat pavilion, its grey interior.

As if he hadn't heard a thing, or understood or cared, Christopher Molyneaux lies back, one arm behind his head. He's gathering his strength. A different kind of silence enfolds him. He knows that punishment awaits, though beyond that he cannot know, only dimly suspect. For now he rests, an incommunicable warmth supporting him. He coughs, arches his back, casts off the blankets Pryor spread last night upon the bed. His other hand drifts over his belly and down, pushing the wool further away, idling. There is about his self-examination and arousal something suddenly fearless, a little menacing, and true.

When I look back, out of my struck portal, at Pryor, half-incorporated with the skull, the sun is both brighter and differently-hued.

It passes overhead, swiftly. Night falls. Another sun rises and sets. Its arc across the sky pivots, days shudder into weeks and months. Colonel Stallbrook and his helpmate dwindle; they're blurred by age and pulsing skies, the lantern-flicker of advancing years. With a wild look, as if at last conceding something known but never said or confronted, they see reflected in the shaman's eyeless abstraction of self the confirmation of their loss: fan-deltaic wrinkles, white hair shrivelling, the skin sucked back, a humbling that now accelerates. Stark, for perhaps one full second, two skeletons – their jaws unhinged, their bones dancing slowly apart – illuminate the onset of a longer night. The lake freezes. Ice calls to ice and Pryor's raised and summoning hand is frosted black.

No trees, no distant school, a greenstick whine as cities pop, scatter. Another order of significance arrives. Air thickens with the charge of glaciers. The former gas solidifies, the mirror plane of my glass eye is crushed and I am fractioned, like a mote among the asteroids. Only the world's ship-like trembling, its great pistons concealed, attests the passage of aeons, time brakeless and unpeopled. Then, as fast as they arrived, faster, the glaciers recede, the waters rise, anoxic bile that boils away at Pryor's still, unvoiced command – and I am either glass again, or obsidian, axe flint, my face upturned and refashioned.

The veil of night draws back. The sun comes close, colossal in the sky. A pale hand hangs me on a wall that rises from the desert's fiery sands.

Other pale shadows brush the lens clear of disaster and I find I'm in a room from which new, old and reassuring forms emerge – the shelves of books, the desk, the built-in cupboard and the bed.

The man upon the bed, gripping the herringbone coverlet holed by moths, the man bald but alive, amazed by his survival into planetary old age, is familiar. It is Alec. Or it is Molyneaux. Or both. It is a *thing* that needs a name.

The room's not as it was before; the sequence of imagining has been altered, even – infinitesimally – the stirring in the drapes.

He lifts the glass of water by his bed and I am cast upon its surface as he drinks, close to the terror of his eye, the nostrils and the yellow skin, the chattering teeth, the white pill on his tongue.

But when he sets the glass down and I'm back in the mirror, I see an apple wobble into existence beside the glass, on a saucer. He picks it up, approaches me and holds it up, offering the fruit of Deauville and the garden of mortality. 'And sir,' he says, the voice remote, radio distressed, like something dialled, 'what if you could really come back, be here in the future, knowing it, much more than if you'd merely conjured an image or cast the runes?'

He bites into the flesh of *Malus sylvestris*. His eyes roll up. Pale presences flush out from every wall to catch him as he falls. White violet skinny claws, warty and hand-painted. An eye, a cloak, a tremolo of creeps: cartoons, the imps and gristly disjecta of Disney, Bosch; a swarming substrate with a will.

Again the voice crackles across the years. It is the witch who calls him now, who calls through him to me. *O! Dip the apple in the brew / And let the sleeping death seep through! / Dip the apple in . . .*

My God, I'm holding it. The apple's real. Green one side, red the other, heavy, bitter as a quince. The stars outside the room! They're clustering. A shining host –

I'm breathing hard; the knowledge that *this is me breathing* makes my heart gallop. It is my heart, my breath. I'm being held – held down, and looking up. I've stopped breathing. My mouth is full. My heart has stopped. A hand closes – is this a hand I know? Has it a face? A hand closes the eyelids in my face.

*

Dear June,

Dr Anthony Stallbrook, my pleasant Jungian (v.s.), quite surprised me the other day. I told him I was growing breasts and he dropped his notebook and said in a low voice that it was no doubt unprofessional of him to say anything but that he 'found all of this personally disgusting'. I assumed he meant not just the breasts, but my whole predicament, sexual relations with men etc – and I was prepared to be disappointed in him, because he is an intelligent person – but not a bit of it. He said that it was the punitive measures he found disgusting, that they were an overcompensation (his word) and that he regarded me, very neutrally, as a 'natural homosexual'. 'As opposed to a mechanical one,' I replied and he laughed: 'I thought you were going to say "unnatural".' And then he stumped me. 'Is sex mechanical, Alec, for you?'

Well, I had to think. Of course I've given some thought to the advantages (and disadvantages) of function divorced from feeling. As which of us has not? After all, beyond a certain point in life, one does not want to go on being hurt. Still, our joshing presented this 'natural' instinct for self-preservation in another light, and I began to have a sense of many aspects of my life as, indeed, some kind of overcompensation – for the loss of C.C.M., I mean, which was to others at the time, no more than the loss of a friend.

If I were to put it in my own terms of the period, Chris's death and the whole routine of burial were the set of 'instructions' I received. And what I made of them constituted a changed 'state of mind'. I changed, I think, from someone into something more like some thing. *A something that had lost a soulmate – maybe even a soul.*

Talking it over with A.S. reminded me of an evening with Chris, when he'd already won his scholarship to Trinity and I had yet to make an impression on King's, or anywhere else for that matter. We were on the river. I was punting, sending the boat first too far to the right and then too far to the left, never in a straight line. Chris said I overcompensated, *trying to correct a wrong steer, and I, being distractable, said that there was something in that – that I was convinced there existed some law of overcompensation in motion – which I should like to go into properly some day. So I took us into a tree and Chris and I ended up in the water. I went back to Wargrave. The next I heard was from Edith Molyneaux, his mother. Chris suffered from TB, about which I knew nothing. He was a pale boy, that's all I'd ever thought, and by this point it was a paleness invested by me with his own integrity and delicacy of mind. It seemed to me a definite strength and not a weakness. One wanted to be more like him. He had an attack on the way home from Cambridge, went to hospital, and died. Much later on, Edith told me he'd been in terrible pain for six whole days before the end.*

Soon after Chris died, a boy at school stole my locked diary. He never divulged the diary's contents, which were hardly shocking – positions of stars, Euclidean parallels, 'neutral' records of chemistry experiments, his (Chris's) attempts to get me to listen to Beethoven – but I was outraged. I read it the other day. There is one mention of my hand brushing against Chris's while we were hanging a pendulum. I suppose I might have blushed for that. I'm sorry to say that I beat that boy rather hard.

At Bletchley, too, didn't we overcompensate *for the extra rotor the Germans put in the machine? All that work! All the work, June, it requires to be sure!*

I have been dreaming of Chris every night since that last session with

A.S, and of course it strikes me forcibly that these dreams are themselves a coded overcompensation, the price paid for a suppressed reality. But – and this is what the man in the mirror appears to be saying – perhaps it is not that way round. Perhaps it is not the code of the dream that has to be broken. Perhaps the dream is not a result of suppression, or anything like that – but is itself a set of instructions, which makes possible the next bit of life.

Sleep allows us to go away and forget about work, and dreams are the way in which we tell ourselves in the meantime how to pick up the thread. A dream is a stored programme. A dream configures me. I wake into a new function.

My dreams are candid with me: they say I am chemically altered. They are full of magical symbolism! At the same time, they are enormously clear – where there is high reason and much thought, there will be much desire and many imaginings. Urges. I can be given drugs and hormones but they will only work as drugs and hormones work. They cannot get at the excess desire. Take out libido and another drive replaces it. Materialism and determinism define me through and through, and yet there is more than they allow. And if that illusion of more – call it free will – is itself a mere effect, then an 'effect' suggests, does it not, a real cause, as a film 'suggests' a projector?

When I dream, I am observing myself. Then I come back into myself when I open my eyes and I wonder what I've done, where I've been. In the latest instalments, Stallbrook got transposed into a schoolmaster, as far as I can recall, and I acquired strange powers. But do I come back, June? Or is a trace of me left in that other world? Does something of the dreamer come back into this one? What of the dead, in dreams? They speak, but are they just my projections, or do they also exist? Do they project?

My breasts at least do not. Though that is the fault of expectation. (Because one does not expect a man to have breasts, they do not appear to resemble them. They are flattish, pouchlike and red; the nipples enlarged, oblate.) I asked Trentham if he would like to see them, and he fairly ran off. I can't say that I blame him.

I am afraid of becoming something else. A hybrid. The fear is not the *change, it is the loss of, well, one's personal past. It is quite like the fear of becoming a machine, in fact. I grieve for Chris now in a way I could not before, and it is precious to me, this new old grief. I fear losing him again in losing myself. I know what you will say. You'll say, Alec, the 'I' is always there. The 'I' does not disappear if you change its data or its sex – its experiences and memories. It is there in the background, the ground-stuff. And even if a clever doctor were able gradually to mechanize it all, and erase my past, he would not have killed me. It's Russell's 'neutral stuff' of the mental and physical worlds, isn't it, but oh, June, it is no neutral matter being caught between them!*

In distress,

A.

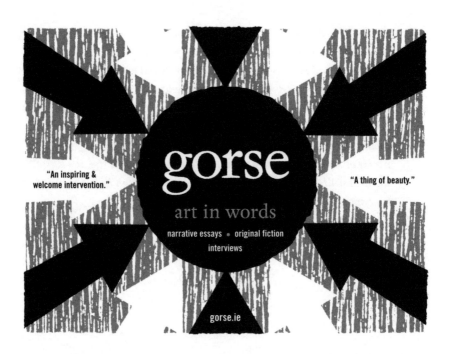

D. NURKSE

Ten Poems

Saturn

I hid and watched
the spider take the fly apart.
Each fragment pulsed with life.

But when the wasp arrived
with his bloated abdomen
I could sense the sting,
the web collapsing,
the cold pang of watching.

I peeked from under the shed
where the great brooms
are painted into tar pots,
the cave of broken shovels.

August with its burden of dragonflies.
I found I could make the clouds pass
faster by narrowing my eyes.
I could make the clock stop
by holding my breath.

I counted backwards
all the way before I was born,
when my parents paced their deck
longing for Tallinn to recede.

So fierce was my patience
I forced the ants to grow old,
baffled and transparent.

I could see my pores through them
when they tried to cross my leg.

My love for their soft feelers
sealed me out of twilight.

At dusk the cat slunk by,
whom I once consorted with and fed
secret foods – brie, cocktail links.

I called him, *Saturn, Saturn.*
But he had a robin in his mouth
and showed me the cleft under his tail

as if I were just another dying thing,
the night wind rattling in the pines.

The Top

When my father died, I dreamt of him,
his plaid flannel shirt, his warm skin
that smelled of sweat and cologne.

My pulse jumped but he warned me immediately,
I am a dream, not a man. Together we span
the red-and-silver top. He held it motionless
and let me whip the kinked string. I was amazed
at my power. I made it stand in loneliness
outside the world, time honed to matter,

then the point splayed, the arc wobbled,
together we shielded it with cupped hands
from its own fall, the tip inscribing
ever larger circles, blatant zeroes.
It fell. He consoled me.

We played pick-up sticks. He said,
since I am a thought and have no weight,
it isn't fair, I won't disturb them,
you take an extra turn. I was aghast
at the violence of my pulse, disrupting
that perfect world created by a spill.

We played 'dawn,' we played 'child wakes
and shouts.' We played 'empty room.'
We played 'cars swishing in the rain
to Bushwick, other children murmuring
behind sheetrock walls, other fathers dying.'
He had warned me: *I'm just a voice.*

Gentians

1

Because my father shouted at me
over the lid to the mustard jar
I made up the story in which he dies.

I dreamt the fallow field,
two pale cleft stones,
the path ending, the wind
the body makes, a beetle
scurrying away, then pausing,
raising a feeler, scuttling back.

I added faint stars.
Because I had to guess their names
Spica and Vega blaze in the wrong quadrant.

The shepherd who will find the body
is confused, turns east at the springhead,
and sees that long shape
like a felled deer or windfall pine.

It's May. On the high screes
the gentians, impossibly dark blue,
open, but only in the mind.

    2
He shouted just once

but the shepherd runs downhill
leaving his flock to graze
the herbs of the clearing –

yarrow, datura, verbena –
because I don't know the names
or which leaf is faintly luminous
and which bristles with fine hair,

a straggler on matchstick legs
strays up to the moraine
at the glacier mouth, there
where the frozen rivers stand
like veins on a sleeper's forehead.

Trespass

1

We sneaked into churches, Mu and I,
to drink the sour communion wine
that May my father died.

We jiggled a wire in tumblers
or slipped a borrowed credit card
between deadbolt and strike plate.

We were scrupulous and did no damage,
retreating if we had to force metal,
splinter wood, or break glass.

We were jealous of our roles:
lookout, lightfoot. Even in Home Room
she angled her quiz away from me.

We erased our footprints
out of respect not fear.

I wanted the blood alone.
Astringency puckered my mouth,
a promised vagueness.

The same *once* –
like a bee swerving from a straight line –
with which my father fell.

He lived Forever before,
Forever Amen afterward,
never in the blind gulp.

Did we long to be caught?

Perhaps no one knew.
Just a few ounces missing,
a loose cork.

2

I admired Mu's courage
yet it scared me.
No one she knew had died.

By June she was lighting
Chesterfields in the nave.

In August she met Wilson Dubrow
whose mom was killed on the Taconic
and started going with him
into the pines behind Sears
to hunt fireflies.

We argued in thin voices.
She began to bring her own wine.

Bali Hai in a hip flask
– whose blood was that? –
and White Owl blunts.

The ash on the slabs horrified me.

Her clothes were changing.
Gauzy halters. And her diet.
Slim Jims in taco sauce.

I found myself going for long walks
very late, all alone,
staring at the steeples.
Zion. Calvary. Mary Star of the Sea.

3

But I'm weak and if I dare walk
by myself to the sacristy
loneliness will force me
to the granite floor
and I'll tell my father
how cold the night is
and how slow.

Ignorance

The pines don't know they are evergreen,
the cedar can't tell it has resinous fronds,
the names aren't sure what they stand for,
and we're heading for a picnic
at Lime Kiln Falls – it's unclear

how you make small talk, undress,
stare up at the ravenous copulating dragonflies,
choose curtains, raise children, knot a rep tie.

We've packed two blue-veined eggs
boiled between six and sixteen minutes,
an apple – Northern Spy or just Delicious –
wrapped in foil, greenish Gouda,
a slice of rye curling into itself

and we sense the falls west of Cold Spring.
Are we happy? Every step we take
requires another – how to ever get there?

How to pick a spot among the thousand spots,
each with its challenge – fire ants, wasps,

spume, load roar, no-view, headache, sunstroke,
nettles, poison oak, strangers, perfection?

Darling, let's bargain in the language of Ignorance
who brought us out of zero, the sulphuric ocean,
with the self-hushed eloquence of the falls
undoing themselves behind a scrim of birches.

Then let's sleep. When we wake
it may still be afternoon.

Marriage in the Orchard Country

Bees conceived us, they danced out our blueprint
and sealed us with propolis. Out of green dust
they fashioned the stranger we adore and follow
so blindly, with such rancour at the plan.
They specialized: undertaker, nurse, guard,
forager, architect, drone for anticipation,
Queen for forgetting. We hardly saw them.
Each had a brain like a sesame seed. They circled
the planet four times, two hundred wing-beats
per second, every act subject, verb, or object.
At dawn a fat dot whined absurdly straight,
as if Euclid's lines were carved in air.
At twilight a sac brimmed with transparency
between pane and sash. Yet it was they
who commanded us, we couldn't know, they made us
new at each breath, they fitted us with desire
as we lay at twilight in our pine bed,
scared to touch each other, longing to,
in these bodies which are flying inwards.

Custody

When the child came prancing in her orange slicker,
I forgot the tipping point, the albedo shift,
the singularity, just guessed she might slip
on the seesaw, or swing too high
and flip over backwards, she might choke
on a stale bagel, she might be bored
and miss her mother. When she left for class,
the sea rose in my mind like a weary guest.
I thought, *that flood is our inner life,*
violence of the future – but the child
came skipping back, so I dreaded the cracks
where she might stumble, how the maple leaves
might dapple her, high beams dazzle her,
the brontosaurus lunch-box would fly open
denting the shrink-wrapped hard-boiled egg,
a pear could roll sideways: even now I fear
her terror at treading the small red ants
who wander in circles carrying their dead.

The Bulletins

1

She says, when the President was shot, I thought, in fifty years I
will remember this: not the bullet entering the chambers of the
mind, but where I was when I heard the news. So I stamped it in my
memory.

I was playing field hockey, scholarship kid at Saint Regis. Knobby
raw knees under my plaid skirt: how could anything be so big but so
skinny? Now the President would never see my cellulite-dimpled
legs. But what could he have done? Forgive me?

The messenger had been running, with wild arm movements and an unearthly slowness, perhaps leery of gopher holes, across the lush sward between us and that pimple-Gothic campus with its lame chapel and spire.

He gasped the news to each section of the field, his chest heaving, his belly contracting, even to the water-girl who stood on the sidelines, clutching her brimming pail.

I thought, at least the game, which I so hated, would be postponed.

But no. The freshman girl stood there, throat working, thighs trembling, spilling a few drops. The game resumed as if of its own volition. The opposing team, brawny seniors from Southwick, raised their taped sticks high. That long twilight, no foul would be called.

2

And now, she says, that sanctified death is an art form, a discipline. You have to specialize. The paraffin test. The throat wound which exists only in the Parkland memo. The shareholders of the company contracted to service the freight elevator at the Texas Book Depository. Jack Ruby's kidney medication. It overflows the threshold of a life. You'd need a dozen selves just to confirm Oswald's trip to Minsk.

Now the Age of Terror. A clique of ecstatic suicides. For each killer, a thousand steady jobs; bankers, publicists, bloggers, documentarians, Security diplomates in office complexes with tinted windows, in leafy suburbs where the streets bear no signs, custodians on server farms.

3

Evening. We're crouching in darkness on our fire escape in Crown Heights, passing a jar of spitwarm wine. Fireflies sometimes climb this high. Satellites are passing, thick as a swarm, as if part of every constellation could detach and dart away.

We know all the names but not the dim blurs they correspond to:
Andromeda, The Scorpion, Draco. Sometimes the brindle cat pads up
to rub against us, and the one who is not being touched is suspended a
moment in jealousy.

She says, Kennedy was so young. In the Crisis, he was overmatched.
It was luck we didn't go to war, chance we're still alive, the choices
of the ticking clock, the breeze in a Levolor blind. Curtis LeMay
burst into the Oval Office, spittle-lipped, shouting, cocksucker, you
missed your chance.

4

Slowly we're getting drunk. Below us, children pass on skateboards,
holding themselves very erect, proud of their silence and
unpredictability. In a single movement, as if unwilled, one will brake
and flip his board into his own hands. Is there no bedtime?

We lived with the end of the world as with a lover: tomorrow we marry,
tomorrow we separate, tomorrow or a few seconds deeper into the next
bulletin. The war that never came was our condom. Now our knees
ache and the cat-scan shows an absence where cartilage should be.

5

It was brutal, she says. All that evening they hit, using both ends of
the stick. I began hitting too, with a strength I didn't recognize.

There was blood on my shin guard, and a piece of tooth, and no one
to signal the end of the quarter, though it was dark, so dark the ball
might be anywhere.

To Live On in Words

after *The Oxford English Dictionary*

'You will find refuge there after death,' my Master said.

They were ranged behind a barrier made from a dead cow's skin. Each had a protective facade, viz. *a monoclinic sulphide of lead, silver, and antimony, usu. occurring as grey prisms with a metallic luster,* designed to repel the unwary.

But there was a back entrance, my Master said. I would float in as breath and take up residence, *one of a family of quadratic curves resembling a conch shell in outline, represented by the equation $(x-a)(x^2+y^2)=b^2x^2$.*

'But when the fire comes, Master? What happens to me?'

'You will be *manifested as a hot bright shifting body of gas, or as incandescence.*'

So I made a home there, eating and sleeping, as once with my father and mother, as once with my wife and child – the same grudging delight, the same copious meals a stranger labors over endlessly, the same long nights, crowded with terrifying or happy dreams, dreams that seem to belong to someone else.

Evening at Chalk Lake

1

Everything the children do is ironic:
Marco! Marco! Polo! Polo!
I'm drowning! I'm saved!

Maybe it's the reflected pines
like shattered down-leading ladders
that make them so double,
or the echo, refined by limestone
and deeply bored mazy water.

It's such a honed sarcasm
soon they'll sing in chorus
we are just children and the game
will close over them like a wave
of backward-sheening bubbles
and dead bees flying down.

2

I'm swimming just outside
the line of tugging buoys.
The guard could whistle me
but he won't: I'm old.

That repartee fascinates me.
But so do the three red mountains:
Hor, Lime Kiln, and Moriah.

There the coyotes egg each other on –
surely their own cry scares them –
and the owl calls, intimate and cold,
adamant as the voice in my mind.

BLOWING OUT AN EGG
aged 12

It was a ritual exercise in care—
to blow out a finch's or blue tit's egg,
transforming the patterned container
of life
into the prize itself. First,
the pin-pricked hole in each end, then
holding it poised to your lips
with nail-bitten fingers and thumbs
like a miniature musical instrument
you were trying to gentle a note from,
pursing your mouth with precise
pressure
to start the albumen's gossamer
lengthening into the toilet bowl. And
after,
if the egg was fresh as it should be,
the pumping gold of what would now
be no singing bird, in small rich gouts
sinking through the water to the
bottom.
And you'd flush that voice away.

NOTES FOR LIGHTING A FIRE

GERRY CAMBRIDGE

£8.00

2nd, paperback, edition
available now from the
Happen*Stance* Press website.
This second edition contains
five new poems not in the
first edition.

www.happenstancepress.com

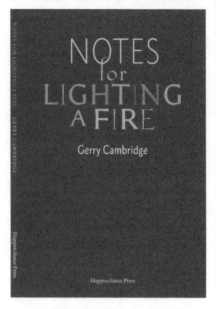

FROM REVIEWS OF THE
HARDBACK EDITION

'[Cambridge's] poetry has something
of Robert Frost's tone and seriousness,
but rings with a deeply personal Scottish
resonance all its own.'
—Rory Waterman,
The Times Literary Supplement

'...poetry of an extraordinary quality...
as fresh as the coldest air of a
winter's night.'
—Alison Brackenbury,
New Walk Magazine

'The language is simple, the effect
beautiful, the craft-work sure. There
is no affected elegance here, only a
genuine elegance in the linguistic
operation of almost every line.'
—John Foy, *Contemporary Poetry Review*

AGOTA KRISTOF
Three Stories

translated by Nina Bogin

My father

You never knew him.

He's dead.

It's for this reason that last year I went away, at the beginning of December, to my country which you don't know either.

Twenty-four hours on the train to reach the capital city, a night of rest at my brother's, and then the train again, for twelve hours, a journey of thirty-six hours to reach the large industrial city where my father was to be immured, in a white porcelain urn, in a small hole hollowed out in the concrete.

Thirty-six hours on the train, with waits and stops, in deserted and cold train stations, surrounded by travelling companions who hadn't lost their fathers, or who had lost them so long ago that they no longer thought about it. I, on the contrary, thought about it, but I didn't believe it.

I had already made this journey several times, when my father was still alive. He would wait for me at the end of my journey, in the suburbs of this industrial city where he had lived so short a time, that he liked so little, and where he had never walked with me, hand in hand.

At his burial, it was almost raining. There were a great many people, wreaths, songs, a choir composed of men dressed in black. It was a socialist burial, without a priest.

I placed a bouquet of carnations near the white urn, so small I couldn't believe my father was inside it, he who had been so tall at the time when I was still his daughter, his child.

The porcelain urn was not my father.

Nevertheless I cried when they placed it inside the concrete. The national hymn was played on a record player. In the hymn God was asked to bless the country and its people who had suffered so much in the past, and for the future as well.

The men's choir had to sing again, because the two grave-diggers were struggling with the covering plate of the vault that wouldn't close. The urn, my father, wouldn't fit inside the little hole in the concrete.

I learned later that my father had wanted to be buried in his native village, not immured in concrete, but they had convinced him – dying from cancer of the stomach, slowly declining in ignorance of his state, relieved by injections of morphine – they had convinced him, my mother and my brother, that he would be better here, in the cemetery of this horrible industrial city that he had never liked, and where he had never walked with me, hand in hand.

Afterwards, I had to greet many people whom I didn't know, but who knew me. The women embraced me.

Finally it was over. Freezing, we were able to go home to my parents' house, that's to say, to my mother's. There was some kind of reception. I ate, like everybody else, I drank. I was tired from my journey, from the ceremony, the guests, everything.

I went into my father's little room where he liked to retire to read, study languages, write in his journal.

My father wasn't there. He wasn't in the garden either. I thought that perhaps he had gone shopping because of all the people in his house. He often did the shopping, he liked doing that.

I waited for him, I wanted to see him again, because soon I would have to return home, I mean, return here. I drank quite a lot of wine, and still he didn't return.

But where has Papa gone? – I asked finally, and everybody looked at me.

My brothers took me to their house, they put me to bed. The next day, I left. Twenty-four hours, thirty-six hours on the train.

During the journey, I made plans.

In a few months, I would come back again, I would pry open the covering plate, I would steal the urn, I would bury it in his native village, beside the river, in the black earth.

It's a region I hardly know, where I have never been. But once I've stolen the urn, where else should I bury it?

There is nowhere that my father walked with me, hand in hand.

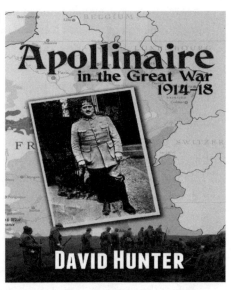

Of a city

It was small and silent, with low houses and narrow streets, without any particular beauty.

I don't know why I speak about it so much, but if I didn't, I would be smothered by the shadow of the mountains surrounding it, high and sombre.

There, sometimes the sky at sundown took on tints that were so extraordinary that people came out of their houses to try to give a name to the colours, which blended together in such a curious fashion that no name ever suited them.

I've already often spoken of that, and also of the house, our house, but I've forgotten the trees in the garden.

On one of the apple trees, from the very beginning of summer, we could pick fruit that was as sweet as honey, even though it wasn't yet ripe. What taste those apples had when they reached maturity, I never knew, because we always ate them beforehand.

This deprives me of a memory, but how could a child know that?

It is late. There, the nights were motionless, the curtains did not sway even slightly in front of the windows, silence drummed in the streets, and we were afraid, because there was always a black and cruel man who hid in the mountains, who walked towards the city and hammered at the double-locked doors.

Before the sun rises, I must speak of everything.

Of the river, of the well with its dark wheel, of the summer, gay and reassuring, of the sun on our faces at five in the morning, of the churchyard.

Autumn, each year, surprised us in the churchyard with a fistful of red leaves that fell all of a sudden from the trees, just when we thought there were still fine days ahead of us.

It was astonishing, they fell and fell, making a pile on the ground that grew deeper and deeper, we walked through them, barefoot, the days were still warm, we laughed, and once again we began to be afraid.

My home

Will it be in this life or in another one?

I'll return home.

Outside, the trees will wail, but they will no longer frighten me, nor will the red clouds, nor the lights of the city.

I'll return home, to a home I never had, or too far back to remember, because it wasn't ever really my home, never.

Tomorrow I will have this home, at last, in a poor neighbourhood in a large city. A poor neighbourhood, for how can one become rich from nothing, when one comes from elsewhere, from nowhere, and has no desire to be rich?

In a large city, for small cities have only a few poor houses; only large cities have an endless number of sombre streets where people like myself can lurk.

I'll walk towards my house through those streets.

I'll walk through those wind-whipped, moon-bathed streets.

Obese women, sitting outdoors to get a bit of fresh air, will watch me pass by without a word. Filled with happiness, I'll greet everybody. Half-naked children will roll at my feet, I'll lift them up in memory of my own children who will be grown up, rich, and happy somewhere. I'll stroke them, those neglected children, and give them rare, sparkling gifts. I'll lift up the drunken man fallen in the gutter, I'll console the woman who runs screaming in the night, I'll listen to her litany of suffering, I'll calm her.

When I arrive at my home, I'll be tired, I'll lie down on the bed, any bed, and the curtains will sway like the swaying of clouds.

Thus the time will pass.

And, beneath my closed lids, images of the bad dream that was my life will flicker past.

But they will no longer harm me.

I'll be home, alone, old, and content.

RYAN VAN WINKLE & J. O. MORGAN
All Signs

Today is a good day to think about Rome. Ancient footprints. Worn leather sandals. Blood and bile sluiced out into the streets. If you were born in the morning, ask yourself: what have you managed to build? If you were born at night, consider how even a paper boat may cut quickly forgotten paths along the gutter.

> (Every country has its Rome: the pinnacle, or else
> the pit, towards which every tributary flows,
> and with that flowing: all the effluence that wants
> for higher life. Although the gold, hammered out
> to near translucence, does eventually flake off;
> scratches are too easily made, exposing all that rot
> so long ignored beneath; while those others who
> live any great way from the core have lost all care
> in such postures; have lost much care in themselves;
> they gather together, form insular groups; they turn
> circles, watch for the lone interloper; are astonished
> when one of their number breaks ranks, and how
> he departs with such abject abandon, to scatter
> confetties of cranes, of lilies, about him as he goes.)

You'll find yourself wanting to pay more attention to the lifted silver sickle of the moon, but it's the shifting of the earth you should be mindful of. If you have forever lived looking out over the circle sea, you should try sleeping tucked in a doorway, once in a while. Otherwise, lower your head, shoulder the construct you never intended to build, and sharpen what horns you have left; now is the time to see red. There are rewards for breaking all the china.

(The question of piercings is paramount: some prefer
to linger in painful reminder of how we may never
maintain true liberty; that though some may dance
unadorned, their picture of freedom is no more
than mere fiction. For we all know it's the gelding
who runs the longest race; that to hold yourself intact
is to lie apart, heavy with underused muscle, alone
within your pig-ploughed field; that sometimes there
are benefits in permitting yourself to be led by the nose.)

♊

You feel inclined to admit you can only get rich by taking from other people. It's best to abort all efforts to give new names to every visible star, to muse on what awaits you in heaven. It's okay sometimes to think only of your own troubles. Before, you were an empty bucket; now you need filling with strong clear liquor, with wet smoke, music, fried chicken. Imagine yourself as a neat set of tracks in the dust, tracks that will soon disappear beneath the lightest push of air.

(Most are separated when still in infancy, and so
grow up never knowing of their doubles or that
they are themselves not whole, except for a niggling
suspicion, felt first at the onset of puberty, that
some *where* there is some *one*, some *other* who
may fully comprehend them, inside and out, and
who with a mere glance sees through their everything,
and knows they too have likewise been examined, that,
for a moment, their similar souls have co-mingled,
spun, and again come apart – yet weightier than before.
These all-too-brief connections occur just as readily
between two shoppers in a hardware store reaching
both for blue methanol, as between two outcasts
combing through the warm red ash for rice grains
spilt from a corner-torn sack. The separation
is always worse this second time around. Most
are able to suppress their new yearning while others
may create a semblance of sanity only by repeating
to themselves in times of anguish: *she is there
and I am here, she is there and I am here, she
is there and I am here* – till balance is restored.)

♋

Childhood was a school of self-disgust and insecurity. You need to reach out and scratch those you love into some kind of wakefulness; things may grow beyond the point where you have any lasting influence if you delay. You have become an easy target for oblivion, sat alone on a raft of rot-wood, adrift on an ocean that's set to expand exponentially.

(When the crisis, long expected, hits,
there's no recourse to the coping devices
built up for your protection. Despite best intentions
of being the last one standing, of beating back
whatever you've been forced to bear, still,
without warning, the carapace cracks
and squeezes your too-soft body out,
now fully exposed to what you know
you cannot hope to endure. All that remains
is to hide away your rawness under stones
till in the dark somehow you find the means
by which to re-harden your skin.)

♌

Late at night you'll wake turgid and sheetless, will understand that kindness is as scarce, as priceless, as the milk of queens. Because there is no moon, and no one will see, you'll find yourself rising, going outside, shrugging your robe to the lawn as you look for the deepest black between the spinning stars. Here is where you draw the draught of milk that asks you for no second gulp. Your friends think you ferocious, in your cravings, in your guile; even they don't know of your timidity, the bleat of fear you muffle with your cloak.

(Out of strength came sweetness, though the bees
didn't grow nor burst from rotting bones, they chose
instead to structure their house amidst the brittle ribs
of the golden corpse – there to manufacture living food;
food which, as milk, need not be killed to be consumed,
both juices freely flowing; though unequal in viscosity.
Now mixed and tinned for your convenience, take care
not to wrap your tongue too tight to the pleasure
of a dunked then swiftly twisted spoon, as you sit
cross-leggèd beneath the lonely spread of tamarisk,
while some scrawny thing, with hunger glowing,
stalks you from within the long dry grass.)

♍

The sky and all its circles tell us that the ones we love must some day take their final leave. This is no shortcoming of the stars, nor is it laziness to remind us of the things we struggle daily to ignore. Simply, you must accustom yourself to the disagreeable taste and texture of another's bread – how bitter it can be, how stringy, how dry. As soon as it feels right to do so: share a long-kept secret with a lover while they sleep; memorise the underlying blueprint of their bones; trace and trace again the soft green highways of their veins. For one day, understand, you will be driving, just driving; you will not be lost, you'll merely realise how, today, you have nowhere to go.

(In the same way it can be hard to differentiate
between the melting sensation stirred in your gut
as your lover passes close and the nausea welled
as your driver feathers the clutch, so is it hard
to be sure that what you feel in interconnecting
your self with that one other self is in any way different
to how you'd feel with another such self so inclined.
Is that ignored uncertainty the best way for any new life
to be begun? If only there were a way to take out
what lies in you and mix it with what lies in her;
a curious *magic* that operates far beyond touch
while you both stand, calmly, before one another,
unmoving but for the shivers that ripple across
your naked skin, that could be mere coolness:
a night breeze slipping in from the balcony; or
some other sensation, growing, as yet unnamed.)

♎

You might spend the day full-ensconced in your bed watching TV in nothing but knickers and vest, dunking chocolate digestives in coffee kept hot in the vacuum flask that you stole when you were still in your teens. This is fine for the world beyond your world is too full of airheads demanding your participation in social engagements they only indulge in because it allows them to feel more connected to people as clueless as they are regarding their need to be seen taking part. Or you might spend all day outdoors, just walking, hands in pockets, while your shadow shrinks to meet you, creeps again outwards behind, to cover up the fallen leaves your restless feet have kicked aside. This too is good for you as you've been feeling very heavy, and you do not wish to give in to the weaknesses built up through lethargy, defeating dizziness by making sure your feet stay active, closer to the ground.

(The shelves may be lined with book after book
on the rules for proper living, written by men
who knew no more nor less than any other men;
while, outside the land is full of beasts, who,
being free, have no recourse to wrongfulness,
are free to fuck or rip each other limb from limb,
who look up with bloodied muzzle for the reproach
that never comes, nor even the shake of a head. But
man feels safe within the houses man alone has built;
can cast out other men who disagree with how
this house is run. And *it is right* to live this way.
Nonetheless, when the door stands open, be it
into frost or mud or sun-hot sands, and you
without your shoes stand on the doorstep looking out,
it is no less right to hitch up your skirts and go.)

♏

It is only an arbitrary conduit towards theoretical recapitulation; don't let yourself get so heated by things beyond your control. People will spit the word *phoney* right in your eye. Even those who live far away, babbling incomprehensibly, understand that a foolish man is a man who hankers after childlike ignorance. Don't worry about the scales that blinker your sight, most will acknowledge you aren't the one to blame. Let yourself listen to songs nobody seems to like but you. Learn it's possible to walk on water; how birds see air as just another fluid to be swum through. Don't broadcast the link; not this time and never again; don't send another positive word into the maw.

(I am the most at risk from my own violence.
A chance remark from you and down I plunge.
I wish to mark my mistakes yet can't come close
in case the poison bubbled up in me somehow
seeps into you. Simple household tools transform
into potential weaponry. If the fruit-knife finds
a skin not fit to bite so its point will turn inward.
I dare not release the pressures built up in my blood.
All I can do to hold myself back is to race on
ahead of my thoughts, there to sever the cord
that connects them to action, whilst trying ever
to repair the faulty link. Don't risk your sensibility
in securing my comfort. You needn't endure this.
I am not fit to know you, nor be friend to anyone.)

All arrows; no target. You hold your head up, stretch the sinew, shoot, because – what else can you do? It might make more sense to close yourself into the basement; to synchronise the beat behind your eyes against the chugging of the pipes. If there is no basement: try the stairs. You are so full of points you can no longer move outside yourself with any honesty. You'd be far better off relinquishing your scattergun approach, to fix your aim on one green apple in an orchard as vast as the sea, as multifarious as stars.

(You may hunt to survive, or for sport, or as
a lonely act of war, though your technique
remains the same for each: your soft footfall,
your muscles taut, intent to kill, your greed
for being *the only one left standing*, till
on pushing aside dry leaves so you see her
bathing in a oil-black pool, overhung by rock.
And as you lift your gun to line its notches
on the scoop of skin between her shoulders
so she turns, and sets her creamy almond eyes
against your blue. She has you now. You're hers.
But she is gentle in her wild possession, lets you
watch her wade yet closer, lets you see
the dark rim of her long lips tightening.
Only then are you able to put down your gun
and back off, forgetting her – letting her be.)

♑

What gets called *new blood* is so often no more than the same old red paint, just thickened and darkened with age. You need to make more of an effort. Delays on the subway will always require you to question your mortality. Make it look like you're checking your watch, and for God's sake don't cry – it won't get you anywhere near where you wanted to go. Push your shoulders back until you can be certain of the tension and length of your spine. Don't fall for the trap of investing emotions in other people's transitory problems. Being mostly water, through and through, remember you know how it feels to be caressed.

(Take two small goats, one fine, one average.
Keep the one of better breeding pure. Allow it
cream instead of milk so that its coat is glossy,
full, so that its softened skin is without spot.
Bring it indoors on cold nights. Sing it to sleep.
Put the lesser beast to the hill; strengthen its gut
with coarse dry grass; let its hair grow tangled,
thick as thorn; fill its belly with young; prolong
its pain in removing its pre-weaned kids, so that
each day it aches to contain such presses of milk.
And then, at the perfect moment, kill the other:
the coddled, virginal, hand-reared animal. Let it
live on in the bound spines of books; as gloves,
fine knitwear; in casseroles, pâté, hors d'oeuvres.
Let its cousin continue unknowingly, just as before:
more kids, more milk, its small neat hoofprints
divergent, repeated, for ever and ever – where
change favours only the fortunate, not the most fit.)

≈

The things we do to try and keep our children good: milk always fresh in the fridge, but you never do know what may turn a child bad. A trip to the play-park ends in the dismemberment of a hitherto favoured plush toy. A bowl of warm apple purée for dessert begs a fire in the toolshed not long after the rains. Some mornings: an orgy of dresses, slapped over the front lawn, brittled by frost. Sometimes your only recourse is to leave them be. If you don't you'll soon find yourself flooded with exhaustion, unable to retaliate, unable to move.

(All light poured in is stripped out by degrees. Red
is the first to go, along with its associated warmth:
the blood drained, thinned to wishy-washy pinks
and peaches, juiceless oranges. Then yellow
gives up quick – as was ever to be expected;
its plasmic aide to the living condition, held back,
so that green is forced out too, can no longer breathe.
Most try to hold position at these easier earlier levels
though some will push on to dwell within blue, peering
over its border into an ever continuing gloom. Even in
the midst of all that nothingness survival is still
possible, so long as the bright beam of your lifeline
remains intact; though you'll need to compress
all of your wits not to fade away into the black,
which sucks as sharply as it penetrates, which can't
be reasoned with, doesn't love you, only hurts.)

The rain comes down so fast one can forgive that inarticulate homesickness for anything-that-matters. As the seas rise think fondly of the whale, easing its bulk with the currents, blowing out hard before each breath new-held. The whale has no great aim, seeks no golden ticket, is as much a part of the stars as the dust it ingests. For weeks the whale is content to hang in a column of water, to press its face to the sheen of kept-out air, to fill its cold cathedral with lament. But here, if it rains for more than you can bear, you will be forgiven if you write in your diary: *stretch me no longer across this rough and presupposing world.*

> (It's like wearing yourself inside out, allowing
> the world to flow over you, through you, to sift
> the mica from the muck, to let that thickness
> in which each small good dwells, pass right on
> and out. Though it is important to move, to stir
> the world-stuff in travelling through it; so that
> what gets taken in is always fresh, is balanced
> by what is given to gain it. With no movement
> the stagnant home-space is soon exhausted
> of anything-worth-having, yet still you go on
> drawing in, to grow fat on mere *stuff,* such
> a bloat you become unrecognisable, till in you
> but a few grains of goodness remain, no more
> than microscopic morsels, adrift in the gloop
> that once was you, as your border dissolves,
> as you join with all that other gloop, drift off,
> to be filtered by a more deserving passer-by.)

FRANCIS PONGE
My Creative Method

translated by Beverley Bie Brahic

In 1947, during a trip to Algeria, Francis Ponge wrote 'My Creative Method' at the invitation of Trivium, *a Swiss magazine. Five years had passed since the publication of* Le Parti pris des choses (The Defence of Things), *his now classic collection of prose poems. Sartre had made the book a springboard for reflections about poetics and philosophy; painters like Braque admired Ponge's close-ups of such prosaic objects and phenomena as a pebble or rain pinging into a courtyard. Although some of his poems, or description-definitions as he calls them in 'My Creative Method' (the title is in English in the original), prove on closer reading to be metaphors for the processes of language itself, and/or manifestoes for a social justice then central to Ponge's thought, at first glance they appear to want only to capture the thing in itself much as a Cubist painter might paint a carafe or guitar from different angles, hoping to catch, if not its essence, at least all its surfaces, those available to the mind's eye as well as those perceived by the naked eye. Ponge was naturally gratified by the attention his poems attracted even as he protested that he had never set out to exemplify the philosophical ideas with which he was being taxed.*

So it was that on Thursday, 18 December 1947, in Sidi-Madani, a cultural centre in Algeria, Ponge sat down to explain, above all to himself, how he worked. Day by day he jotted his thoughts, searching or tongue-in-cheek, in a journal, ever ready to pique his admirers further – in the end by publishing the journal with all its repetitions, revisions and half-formed thoughts as the finished essay, the text as object. As an unpublished preface (apology?) by Fritz Meyer, a Trivium *editor, says: 'Look at the sculptor: in the evening he wraps his sculpture up in a sheet that he takes off next morning to go back to it, there it is. It is the same*

for F.P.: he doesn't write from one end to the other (beginning–end),
he is forever right in the middle . . .' In later texts, The Glass of Water,
for instance, Ponge was to adopt the publication of the work-in-progress
with all its afterthoughts as one of his signature styles.

'My Creative Method' opens modestly. Falsely-modestly: 'No doubt
I am not very intelligent: in any case ideas are not my strong point.'
The slipperiness of the double negative shadows the opening sentence of
Valéry's Monsieur Teste: *'Stupidity is not my strong point.' It also tilts*
at the French intellectual establishment whose devotion to the analytical
triad of thesis-antithesis-synthesis and a certain abstraction were to be
deconstructed by Ponge's thingy-ness and exposed-seams writing style.
Not the finished thought with its trompe l'oeil clarity but the messiness
of the thought as it comes into being and is elaborated, maybe discarded,
will become Ponge's mot d'ordre – or disorder. In 'My Creative Method'
we see Ponge working this out, looking back at how he wrote Le Parti
pris des choses *and forward, perhaps unwittingly, to the later works.*
– B.B.B.

Sidi-Madani, Thursday, 18 December 1947

No doubt I am not very intelligent: in any case ideas are not my strong point. I've always been disappointed by them. The most well-founded opinions, the most harmonious philosophical systems (the best constituted) have always seemed to me utterly fragile, caused a certain revulsion, a sense of the emptiness at the heart of things, a painful feeling of inconsistency. I do not feel in the least assured of the propositions that I sometimes have occasion to put forth in the course of a discussion. The opposing arguments almost always appear just as valid; let us say, for the sake of precision, neither more nor less valid. I am easily convinced, easily discouraged. And when I say I am convinced: it is, if not of some truth, at least of the fragility of my own opinion. Furthermore, the value of ideas appears to me most often in inverse proportion to the enthusiasm with which they are expressed. A tone of conviction (and even of sincerity) is adopted, it seems to me, as much in order to convince oneself as to convince one's interlocutor, and even more, perhaps, *to replace* conviction. To replace, so to speak, the truth which is absent from the propositions put forth. I feel very strongly about this.

Hence, ideas as such seem to me to be the thing I am least capable of, and they are of little interest to me. You will no doubt object that this in itself is an idea (an opinion) . . . but: ideas, opinions seem to me controlled in each individual by something completely other than free will, or judgement. Nothing appears to me more subjective, more epiphenomenal. I really cannot understand why people boast of them. I would find it unbearable should someone try to impose them on us. Wanting to give one's opinion as objectively valid, or in the absolute, seems to me as absurd as to state, for example, that curly blond hair is *truer* than sleek black hair, the song of the nightingale closer to the truth than the neighing of a horse. (On the other hand I am quite given to formulation and may even have a certain gift in this direction. 'This is what you mean . . .' and generally the speaker agrees with my formulation. Is this a writer's gift? Perhaps.)

It is somewhat different for what I shall call observations; or shall we say experimental ideas. It has always seemed to me desirable to agree, if not about opinions, at least about well-established facts, and if this still seems overly pretentious, at least about a few solid definitions.

It was perhaps natural that with such a disposition (disgust for ideas, a taste for definitions) I should devote myself to recording and defining the objects of the world around us, and particularly those which constitute the familiar universe of our society, in our time. And why, it will be objected, repeat tasks which have been done already, and more than once, and firmly established in dictionaries and encyclopedias? – But, I shall reply, why and wherefore is it that several dictionaries and encyclopaedias co-exist in a given language, and yet their definitions fail to correspond? Why, above all, why do they seem more concerned with the definition of words than with the definition of things? Where do I get this impression, which is all in all quite preposterous? What causes the difference, this inconceivable gap between the definition of a word and the description of the thing designated by the word? Why is it that dictionary definitions seem so lamentably lacking in concreteness, and that descriptions (in novels and poems, for example) seem so incomplete (or too particular and detailed, on the contrary), so arbitrary, so random? Could one not imagine a sort of writing (new) which, situating itself more or less between the two genres (definition and description), would take from the first its infallibility, its indubitability, its brevity also; from the second its respect for the sensory aspect of things . . .

Sidi Madani, Saturday, 27 December 1947 (1)

1

If ideas disappoint me, do not agree with me, it is because I too willingly agree with them, since that is what they want, what they are made for. Ideas demand my assent, insist on it, and it is too easy for me to give in: this gift, this agreeableness, gives me no pleasure, but rather a certain revulsion, nausea. Objects, landscapes, events, people around give me a great deal of pleasure on the other hand. They convince me. By the very fact they don't need to. Their presence, their obvious solidity, their thickness, their three dimensions, their palpability, indubitability, their existence of which I am far more certain than of my own, their: 'that's not something you invent (but discover)' side, their: 'it's beautiful because I couldn't have invented it, I would have been quite incapable of inventing it' side, all that is my sole reason to exist, my *pretext*, so to speak; and *the variety of things is in reality what makes me what I am*. This is what I want to say: their variety makes me, allows me to exist even in silence. Like the space in which they exist. But in relation to just one of these things, in relation to each particular thing, *if I consider just one of them*, I disappear: it annihilates me. And, if it is only my pretext, my raison d'être, if it is therefore necessary that I exist, from it, it will only be, it can only be by a certain creation of my own with a thing or things as my subject.

What creation? *The text.*

And, to start off, how do I imagine it, how could I have imagined it, how do I conceive of it?

Through works of art (literary).

Sidi-Madani, Saturday, 27 December 1947 (2)

2

The imitation of artistic heroes. (Exemplary existences. Disgust for sordid compromises. Yet, the experience that compromise is necessary. A sense of measure. Balance.) The love of glory. The love of heroes (and of poets), to distraction. I love my schoolbooks (the Anthologies). Latin writers.

What I conceive of as such: a work of art. Whatever modifies, brings variety to, changes-something-in-the-language. Quite different from a bunch of warrior heroes!

This is *another* reality, *another* outside world, it too giving me more pleasure than it demands (the scandalous aspect, the provocation of novelty in art. Difference between artistic novelty and a paradox); which also gives me a reason to exist, and whose variety is also formative (forms me as a *reader*) (a reader of poems).

But, here too, *each of them* repulses me, rubs me out (erases), annihilates me. I need to exist. I must create something that has to do with them (difference, originality).

Here then is the sort of creation I conceive of with regard to the outside world, quite naturally: *a creation of an artistic, literary order.*

3

As you can see: here I come back to my distaste for ideas and my taste for definitions.

What I shall attempt will therefore be on the order of a definition-description-literary work of art.

4

It so happens that I am capable of this. How does this happen? Why?

What is this thing called talent?

Sidi-Madani, Saturday, 27 December 1946 (3)

I began (really[1]) by saying that I would never be able to explain myself. How is it I no longer keep to this (this position)?

For no, truly, now, I do not believe it at all impossible, nor the least dishonourable, silly, false or grotesque (vain) to attempt to explain myself.

On the contrary I find it very pleasant (when someone asks me to or suggests it) and I should now find it somewhat ridiculous to respond with a proud refusal on principle. That is what would appear silly, false and grotesque to me. It is less silly to risk ridicule than to refuse it obstinately on principle. Hard to avoid . . . !

So what has changed?

---

1 First line of the first text of my first volume (*Douze Petits Ecrits*, N.R.F., 1926).

What has changed is my existence with respect to others, it is that a work[2] exists, and has been talked about. Having been set forth, it has compelled recognition as a distinct existence, and as my 'personality' somewhat too. Thus these *things*: my literary work, my personality, I can now consider as distinct from me, and listen to (respond to) the *a minima* call of their objections to certain interpretations that have been given of them. I need to correct false interpretations (or definitions) of them.

In general the explications of my work and of myself are of a philosophical (metaphysical) nature, and not so much aesthetic or strictly speaking literary (technical). It is this philosophical status that I would gladly take a few pokes at, to begin with.

Nothing more astonishing (for me) than my appeal to philosophers: because truly I am not intelligent, ideas are not my thing, etc. But, after all . . .

Sidi-Madani, Saturday, 27 December 1947 (4)

. . . I am lazy, and look, even for this text, I am persuaded that I don't really have to feed it puffed-up original or new ideas, march them out in serried ranks, varied and coherent, etc. (hosts of them).

I am convinced, for it to be good, it will suffice that I not get too hot and bothered about the topic. I must especially (rather) not write too much, a very small amount each day and more or less as it comes, without fatigue, the flowers of the field. Then, manage to make of that a somewhat original literary object, different from the rest, amusingly lit up, awkward in my manner, which has a life of its own (there aren't umpteen ways of accomplishing this: you have to cut out the explanations).

And that's it, it will do the trick. It will be a stylish little thing.

Right! Let's stop there for today.

Sidi-Madani, Sunday, 28 December 1947

What is this about? Well, if you've been following me, about creating literary objects in such a way as to give them the best possible chance, I don't say of living, but of holding their own (*s'objecter*, to stand up against objectively) for generations, of keeping their interest (as the outside objects themselves will keep their interest), remain at the disposition of future generations'

---

2 *Le Parti pris des choses* (The Defence of Things), 1942.

desire and taste for the concrete, as (mute) opposable evidence, or of the representative (or presentative).

Human objects are what I have in mind, things made and set down especially for man (and by man), but which achieve an exteriority and complexity, and at the same time the presence and evidence of natural objects. But that may be more touching, if possible, than natural objects, because human; more decisive, more apt to be approved by us.

And is it necessary – as some would have us believe – that they be abstract rather than concrete? That is the question . . . (Rendered stupid by the prefect's visit, I could not go further . . .)

Sidi-Madane, Monday, 29 December 1947

(Today it's the lack of the mail and our worrying because of it that kept me from . . . So I decided to call Paris by radio, and now, everything is fine!)

It is therefore descriptions-definitions-literary-artistic-objects that I mean to formulate, that is, definitions which, instead of referring (for such and such a plant, for example) to this or that pre-established (agreed-upon) classification and in sum to some supposedly known (and generally unknown) human science, refer, if not to complete and utter ignorance, at least to a fairly common, habitual and elementary order of knowledge, establish unexpected correspondences, which upset the usual classifications, and thus present themselves in a more striking, sensible and also more pleasing manner.

At the same time, the characteristics of this, that or another object we choose to elaborate upon will preferably be such as have not previously been remarked. If in this way we manage to give our authentic impression and naïve, childish classification of things, we will have renewed the world of objects (of the subjects of literary works of art). And as it is likely that, however subjective and original it may be, our childish impression is nonetheless akin to that of several contemporary or future minds or sensibilities, we shall be heard and thanked, admired.

But must we, so as to render them more striking and susceptible to approval, tend towards the abstraction of these qualities? There, again, is the rub. Well, here, to an important degree, the answer seems to be *yes*. (Develop this point.)

Let us glance, also, at the dictionaries available to us.

On the one hand, there is the Larousse (or Encyclopaedia).

On the other, Littré.

Their difference is significant. And our preference for one over the other, the fact that we use one rather than the other will also be significant.

(Here treat the vocabulary question in detail.)

As for syntax, prosodic forms and rhetoric in general, here again their renewal will be instinctive, and unembarrassed (prudent, nonetheless, and taking only the result, the efficacy into account).

But before all that, it should be noted that our experience of recent successes (and failures) in the matter of literary glory has been most instructive (Mallarmé, Rimbaud).

We have noted that in such matters boldness *paid*.

In sum, here's the important point: THE DEFENCE OF THINGS [*PARTI PRIS DES CHOSES*] *equals* TAKING WORDS INTO ACCOUNT [*COMPTE TENU DES MOTS*].

Certain texts will have more PPC in their alloy, others more CTM . . . no matter. In any case, there must be *both*. Otherwise, nothing will have been accomplished.

(This is but one of the rubrics:)

'Start from words and go towards things.' (Rolland de Renéville): well, that's wrong.

We shall be reproached in some quarters with getting our ideas from words (from the dictionary, puns, rhymes, and what-have-you . . .): but yes, we admit it, this is a necessary procedure, one must respect the raw material, foresee how it will age, etc. (Cf. the *Propos Métatechniques*, already.) Still we shall respond that this is not everything, that we also expect a spontaneity of contemplation and a kind of cynicism, an unembarrassed frankness of relations, to give us our ideas too.

Chosen genre: aesthetically and rhetorically adequate definition-descriptions.

Limits of this genre: its *extension*. From the formula (or concrete maxim) to a *Moby-Dick* sort of novel, for example.

Here we can explain that these days we have pretty much lost the habit of considering things from a somewhat eternal point of view, serene, sirien (from Sirius) that . . .

(To be inserted with the criticism of ideas as such. After: 'a certain revulsion, a sense of the emptiness at the heart of things, a painful feeling of inconsistency, non-resistance, defeat').

Defeat or victory (in a theoretical discussion not followed by a vote, a precise outcome which changes the outside world) defeat or victory (I say) is all the same thing: one is as random, ephemeral, susceptible to change as the other.

And, of course, this inconsistency, this cowardly and disquieting side of even the winning ideas I put forth, I *myself* suffer from it. I myself am defeated, barely exist any more, judge myself refutable, even more humiliated than by a physical defeat. My self-esteem takes a blow.

How then should I agree to spend my life in this condition: in a place overrun with error, full of wind, scaffolding that the flick of a finger can bring crashing down? What is this cotton, this mishmash in my head? Even when it is victorious.

A beautiful image, on the other hand, a bold representation, new and true: of this I am prouder than if I had established a system, made a first-class mechanical invention, beat a record, discovered a continent: it is as if I had discovered a new metal, better yet: I have found it *within man*, and it is signed: it is me, it is the proof of my superiority over the whole world (I am sure, by experience, of the admiration of my peers): I have given delight to the human mind.

. . . Give delight to the human mind.

Not only given to see, given delight to the sense of sight (to the mind's eye), no! delighted the sense which is located in the back of the throat: halfway between the mouth (between the tongue) and the ears. And which is the sense of formulation, of the Word.

What comes of this has more authority than anything else in the world:

the Law and the Prophets come of this. This sense which delights even more when one reads than when one listens (but also when one listens), when one recites (or declaims), when one-thinks-and-one-writes-it-down.

Looking-in-a-manner-that-speaks.

In the beginning a certain naivete no doubt (or stupidity).

If *ideas* (by this do I mean opinions? – maybe) provoke some revulsion in me, a sort of light nausea (this is a fact), it is no doubt that I am not very intelligent. Instinctively, I give them an absolute value, whereas they obviously have only *tactical* value. Hence they cannot fail to disappoint me. The fact is they do disappoint me.

If I happen to emit some, as I do with the same naivete, without attending to their sole tactical value, and pushed on the contrary by who knows what momentary conviction (?), I soon have reason to regret it. Of course! Whose fault is that? It was inevitable.

Hence ideas are not my strong point. Someone who manipulates them effortlessly can always keep one jump ahead: by means of rhetoric. They manipulate me. This infuriates me. I feel duped. And what am I going to prefer to them?

Well now! The same naivete gives me the desire to hear more about facts, observations – or at least about definitions. Though, obviously, it is hardly a question of reaching an agreement about them, but only to discuss, and in the end, to inspire respect, which is why, naturally, no definitions needed: quite the contrary!

A certain stupidity and a lot of whoring around (coquetry). I should like to please everybody.

As you see, I haven't a clue!

Let's get straight to the point. Or, if you prefer, let's try to get caught red-handed, in the act of creation. Here we are in Algeria, trying . . .

Let's get caught in the act of creation.

Here we are in Algeria, trying to render the colours of the Sahel (seen across the Mitidja, at the foot of the Atlas Mountains). It is, therefore, a sort of expressive task.

After much trial and error, we come up with the idea of pinks that are a little *sacripant*. *A priori* the word satisfies us. Nevertheless, we consult the dictionary. It refers us almost immediately from Sacripant to Rodomont (these are two characters in Ariosto): now Rodomont means Red-Mountain and he was king of Algeria. Which is to say, *Nothing could be more appropriate.*

Lessons to be drawn from this:

a) We can use *sacripant* as an adjective of colour. It is even advisable.

b) We can modify *rodomont* by using it in much softened form: '*la douce rodomontade*'. In any case, we are going to be able to work with this.

Ideas are not my strong point. I don't handle them with ease. Rather, they handle me. Give me a certain revulsion, or nausea. I don't much like to find myself thrown among them. The objects of the outside world on the other hand ravish me. They may sometimes surprise me, but they never ever seem to worry about my approval: it is granted them immediately. I do not call them in question.

I have not published much other than a little book called *Le Parti pris des choses*. That was five or six years ago. And it happens that a few people, having read it, asked me for explanations, hoping particularly that I would reveal something of my creative method, as they say.

Naturally I find this extremely pleasant. A little embarrassing as well, to be honest, but I should have expected as much.

Of course, if I wish to be perfectly sincere, I do not conceive that one can validly write other than as I do.

The first question that I shall ask is this: how can one write?

Monday, 5 January 1948 (2)

Let me say it, *finally* – for bit by bit it will be seen that I am beginning by the end – let me say then to begin: any old pebble, for example, *this one*, that I picked up the other day in the bed of the Chiffa wadi, seems to me the occasion for new statements of the greatest interest. And when I say *this one* and *of the greatest interest*, here's what I mean: this stone, since I conceive of it as one of a kind, gives me a particular feeling, or perhaps more a complex of particular feelings. The first thing to realise is this. Whereupon you shrug and deny such exercises have any sort of interest, for, you say, this has nothing to do with man. So what does it have to do with? Well, with man, but up to now unknown by man. A quality, a series of qualities, a compound of qualities not yet written about, unformulated. That's what makes it so interesting. It concerns the man of the future. What could be more interesting? It enthralls me. Why does it so enthrall me? Because I believe I can do this. On what condition? On condition I stick to it, and obey *it*. That I am not easily satisfied (or go too far). That I say nothing except what is suitable to it alone. It is not so much a question of saying all there is to say: that would be impossible. But only what is appropriate to it alone, only what is true. In fact: it is only a question of saying one true thing. That is plenty.

So here I am with my pebble, which intrigues me, touches unknown springs in me. With my pebble that I respect. With my pebble for which I want to substitute an adequate logical (verbal) formula.

Fortunately 1st it lasts, 2nd my feeling at the sight of it lasts, 3rd the Littré is not far off: I have a feeling that the right words can be found there. If they turn out not to be there, I shall have to create them. But in such a way that they communicate, that they conduct thoughts (as one says conduct heat or electricity). After all I have the syllables, the onomatopoeias, I have the letters. I'll figure something out!

And I really think that the words will suffice . . .

This pebble was victorious (won the victory of existence, individual, concrete, the victory of catching my eye and being born into words) because it is more interesting than the sky. Not completely black, more dark grey, as big as half a rabbit liver (but no rabbit is needed here), fitting the palm of my hand. In practice my right hand, with a hollow into which the right side (facing me) of the tip of my middle finger comfortably fits.

Nothing more banal than what has happened to me, nor simpler than the solution to the problem in front of me.

My little book: *Le Parti pris des choses*, having come out almost six years ago, has since then given rise to a certain number of critical articles – on the whole rather favourable – which have made my name familiar in certain circles even beyond France.

Although the very short texts of which this slim volume is composed don't explicitly contain any philosophical, moral, aesthetic, political or other thesis, most of its commentators have interpreted it in relation to these different disciplines.

More recently, two or three critics have finally tackled the study of the form of my texts.

The review *Trivium* published one of these studies and as I expressed my satisfaction, it asked me to comment on what one of my kindliest critics, Mrs Betty Miller, calls my creative method.

'Speaking to poets,' Socrates says, 'I took those of their poems which seemed crafted with the greatest care; I asked them what they had intended to say, for I wished to be instructed by them. I am ashamed, Athenians, to tell you the truth; nonetheless I must tell you. Of all those there present, there was scarcely anyone who wasn't able to give a better account of these poems than those who had written them. I quickly realised therefore that it is not reason which directs the poet, but a sort of natural inspiration, an enthusiasm similar to that which transports soothsayers and fortune-tellers; they all say extremely beautiful things, but they understand nothing of what they say. This, in my opinion, is what poets feel also, and I perceived at the same time that their talent for poetry made them believe that they were also for all the rest the wisest of men; which they weren't. So I left them too, persuaded I was superior to them . . .

. . . 'Finally, I spoke to the artists. I was aware that I understood pretty much nothing about art, and I knew that I would find among them an in-finity of marvellous knowledge. In this I was not mistaken, for they knew things that I didn't know, and in this they were more skilful than I. But, Athenians, the great artists seemed to me to have the same defect as the poets, for there was not a single one of them who, because he excelled in his art, did not believe himself well-versed in other areas, even the most important, and this failing quite overshadowed their skilfulness. So then I questioned myself . . . asked myself whether I would prefer to be as I am, without their skills and without their ignorance, or to have their advantages and shortcomings. I told myself . . . that I would rather be as I am.'

What do we conclude from the above if it is not (excuse me) a certain foolishness on the part of Socrates? What an idea, to ask a poet what he meant to say. And isn't it evident that if he is the only one who can't explain this, it is because he cannot say it any other way (or no doubt he would have said it differently)?

And I extrapolate also a certitude about Socrates' inferiority with respect to poets and to artists – not his superiority.

For if Socrates is, in effect, wise insofar as he is aware of his own ignorance and knows only that he knows nothing, and in effect Socrates knows nothing (other than that), the poet and the artist on the other hand know at least *what* they have expressed in their most carefully wrought works.

They know it better than those who can explain it (or pretend they can), for they know it *in its own terms*. Besides, the whole world learns it in these terms and easily remembers it.

From this we shall soon deduce a number of consequences (or consecutive ideas). But we must first confess that poets and artists do very often abandon their happiness and their wisdom, and believe they are able to explain their poems and furthermore that their skill in this technique renders them apt to speak out on other sorts of problems, which is not the end of the world.

Don't anyone expect me to be so presumptuous. Anyone is more capable than I of explaining my poems. And clearly I am the only one who is unable to do so.

But perhaps the fact that a poem cannot be explained by its author is not to the disgrace of the poem and its author, but to their glory?

What would be embarrassing perhaps, is if someone else said better than I what I had meant to say and persuaded me of a defect (or lack) or on the contrary of a redundancy, that I might have avoided. Personally, I would immediately correct this error, for the perfection of the poems matters more to me than some sentiment of my own infallibility.

But, finally, might one not say that a poem which cannot be explained is by definition a perfect poem?

No, not so. Other qualities are needed, and perhaps only *one* quality. Socrates was perhaps not so silly as he might at first have seemed. And perhaps it wouldn't have occurred to him to ask for the explanation of a poem *that brought its* evidence *along with it* . . . (But would one still have called this a poem? . . .)

What is this evidence? Some virtue of the writing itself (of the means of expression)? Yes, no doubt, in one sense, but in one sense only. It also has something to do with a kind of fitness, a respect for, an equilibrium (this is the most delicate) between the expression (in respect to itself absolutely perfect) and the perfection of the object (or of an object) envisaged.

Egoism and charity are mixed up together here. It is necessary to be at once ferocious and respectful. The means is for the thing itself be to be ferocious . . . and nevertheless fit the norms, the human categories. (It can do no less.)

– So? So!

– Is that it? Amen! . . .

1st Though of my virtues I believe you the closest (*the most particular well expressed . . .*)

Forget commonplaces, you are made for them (. . . *create commonplace*).

2nd Only *what is not well-conceived* (the most particular) is interesting to express.

Let what is not well conceived speak for itself! (in the optative.)

3rd One conceives of the most particular (better) (especially) (only) *apropos of the outside world.* It is the one over there, it is the more particular one here that brings with it its evidence, its powerful desire for expression (its demand for expression), and its confrontable objectivity.

Sidi-Madani, Saturday, 31 January 1948

At every moment of the work of expression, as one writes, language reacts, proposes its own solutions, incites, comes up with ideas, helps in the formation of the poem.

No word is used that is not immediately considered as a person. Its particular lighting effects utilised; and also the shadows it carries with it.

Whenever I admit a word, whenever I let a word go, right away I must treat it not as any old element, a scrap of wood, a puzzle piece, but as a token or figure, a person in three-dimensions, etc . . . and I cannot play with it exactly as I wish. (Cf. Picasso's remark about my poetry.[3])

Each word compels my (and the poem's) recognition of it in all its thickness, with all its associations of ideas (that it would have were it alone, on a dark background). And yet, it is necessary to free it . . .

ABOUT TWO PERSONAL MECHANISMS.

The first consists in placing the chosen object (say how it is *duly* chosen) in the centre of the world; that is, at the centre of my 'preoccupations'; in opening a kind of trap-door in my mind, in thinking about it naively and with fervour (love).

Say that it is not so much the object (it is not necessary that it be present) as the idea of the object, including the word that designates it. It is the object as notion. It is the object in the French language, in the French mind (an item really in the French dictionary).

And at that point a certain cynical relationship is established. Cynicism is not the word (but it needed to be said).

Everything that has been thought is taken into account. All that will be thought and the dimensions of the object, its comparative qualities. Especially the most tenuous, the least habitually proclaimed, the most shameful

---

3 Translator's note: 'You, your words, they're like little pawns, you know, little statuettes, they turn and each word has several sides, and they illuminate each other.' From Ponge, 'The Practice of Literature'.

(either because they appear arbitrary, puerile – or because they evoke a relation which is usually forbidden).

At other times, it is only *one* quality of the object, my favourite reaction, my preferred association with it (peeling the boiled potato – and the way it cooks) which will be emphasized, to which all the importance will be given.

One dips in and discovers things. Here we are dealing with the trap-door of dreams and of sleep, as much as with a clear mind and wakefulness.

Nor must one let oneself be put off by associations customarily forbidden. This is even the main (or principal) task: admit the anomalies, shout them out, celebrate them, name them: a new *character*.

Yes, it is a question of the thing's character, seen in the right light, praised, applauded, approved, considered as a lesson, an example.

One point which must be attentively considered is the following:

I said earlier we were talking about the object as an idea, or notion, to which its name contributes in a very grave and serious way, the French word that usually designates it.

Yes. Of course.

Therefore, the name sometimes helps me, as when I invent some justification for it or appear (persuade myself) to discover it.

But it may also happen that this *partial* group of qualities which are concerned more with the name of the object than with the object itself become too important. This can be a trap.

As for the qualities of the object which depend less on its name than on something entirely other, my attempt to express these qualities must come more *in opposition to the word* which would blur them, which would tend to annihilate them, replace them, put them in a box (pre-package) over-hastily, after having simplified, folded, condensed them excessively.

And here's another way to go about it: consider it unnamed, unnameable, and describe it so well *ex nihilo* that it be recognised. But let it be recognised only at the end: so that its name is something like the last word of the text, and only appears at that point.

Or only appears in the title (given afterwards).

The name must be superfluous.
Replace the name.

Here, however, other dangers can emerge. Avoiding saying the name can transform the poem into a kind of game in such a way that, as game, and therefore lacking in seriousness, the result may resemble one of Abbot Delille's famous periphrases.

Whereas it is not so much a question of making a comparison, *ex nihilo*, as of letting the object speak for itself; allowing it to express its mute character, its lesson, in more or less moral terms. (There must be a little of everything: definition, description, morality.)

One rhetorical form per object (i.e., per poem).

If one cannot really say that the object speaks for itself (personification), which would furthermore constitute a over-facile rhetorical form and become monotonous, nevertheless each object must impose its own rhetorical form on the poem. No more sonnets, odes, epigrams: the form of the poem must in some way be determined by its subject.

Not much in common between this and calligrammes (Apollinaire's): the form must be much better hidden than that.

. . . Which is not to say that I do not sometimes employ certain typographical artifices;

– nor am I saying that in every one of my texts there must be a connection between the form, shall I say prosodic, and the subject treated;

. . . still sometimes this happens (more and more frequently).

All this must remain hidden, must be very much part of the skeleton, never apparent; or even sometimes only in the intention, in the conception, in the foetus: in the manner in which one begins to speak, preserved – then left behind.

No rules: since, in point of fact, the rules change (according to the subject).

Sidi-Madani, Saturday, 31 January 1948

PLAN – Poems, not to be explained (Socrates).

Superiority of poets over philosophers:

a) (I don't really know if poet is the right word),

b) (superiority as long as they don't believe themselves superior in anything other than their poetry.)

Manifestations of poetry. Obviously this is subject to caution. Here is the risk. Poetic knowledge (poetry and truth).

From the particular to the general.

(Inclusion of humour: lots of wordplay.)

Two things are the mark of truth:

action (science, methodology), poetry (damn this word);

reservations?

– *observation of expressive relationships.*

If I define a butterfly as a *superfetatious petal*, what could be more *true*?

Poems, not to be explained:

1st Poem-poems: because not logical. Objects.

2nd Poem-formulas: clearer, more striking, decisive than any explanation.

Superiority of poets over philosophers: they know what they are expressing in its own terms.

From the particular to the general:

the particular in the outside world;

one rhetorical style per object;

all language always tends towards the proverbial.

Sidi-Madani, Tuesday, 3 February 1948, during the night (1)

Nothing more flattering than what has happened to me, but it still makes me laugh! The times have to be bizarrely lacking in interest for people to get attached to my sort of literature! How can they be so mistaken?

Never, in composing the texts, some of which make up *Le Parti pris des choses*, never did I do anything other than have fun, when I was in the mood, writing only what can be written without effort, about the most ordinary objects, chosen completely at random.

Really, the task was conceived light-heartedly, without any profound intention and even to be honest without the least seriousness.

I never said anything but what ran through my head on the spur of the moment or I said it about quite ordinary objects, chosen perfectly at random.

As, for example, these prickly pears . . .

Sidi-Madani, Tuesday, 3 February 1948, during the night (2)

I am not a great writer, Gentlemen, you are mistaken. Next to La Fontaine (for instance), I shall never be anything other than a small boy. I construct with difficulty, build with a great deal of heaviness. True, I do go to a lot of trouble . . . (my pen spits up violently at this point).

. . . This big blot so as to give me the lie and force me to abandon this speech, – and my humility!

Sidi-Madani, Tuesday, 3 February 1948 (in the morning)

In fact I am surely very fortunate, for to tell the truth I am not so much asked to explain one or another of my pieces of writing as to reveal something of the method by which I produce them. And maybe I am permitted to think they are therefore clear enough to be recognised for what they are, recognized as *inexplicable* and therefore people limit themselves to asking me to explain how I managed to produce *such inexplicable* texts, so manifestly clear, so obvious.

Truly, this request has something astonishing about it. Because how does it happen that people be so surprised (or interested) by the obvious nature of a text, to the point of inquiring how it was produced?

How to explain this, other than by a widespread impotency or awkwardness when it comes to writing clearly, a desire to learn how to write like this?

Must I therefore conclude from this request a certain imbecility (or too great complexity) in the minds of the time?

But perhaps I can infer – (which, after all, I should prefer) – something quite other.

Which is that certain of my texts, clear as they seem, have an element of the unexpected, the surprising – and that the astonishment they provoke (and the ensuing questions) are not so much related to their obviousness as to their strangeness? . . .

I should therefore have to conclude there are two sorts of obviousness: the common, which provokes no questions, and the strange (which surprises even as it convinces).

Perhaps by degrees I shall arrive at my meaning . . .

PROÊME – The day people finally come around to admitting the sincerity and *truth* of my persistent declarations to the effect that I do not see myself as a poet, that I *utilise* the poetic magma *but* only so as to rid myself of it, that I am more concerned to convince than to charm, that my self-imposed task is to arrive at formulas both *clear* and *impersonal*,

I will be happy,

I will be spared a lot of useless discussions, etc.

My penchant is for definition-descriptions which account for the present content of notions,

– for me and my fellow citizens (both up-to-date in the book of Culture, and honest and authentic in their study of themselves).

My book must replace: 1st the encyclopaedic dictionary, 2nd the etymological dictionary, 3rd the analogical dictionary (it doesn't exist), 4th the dictionary of rhymes (interior rhymes, as well), 5th the dictionary of synonyms, etc., 6th all lyrical poetry based on Nature, objects, etc.

Desiring to give *a complete account of the content of their notions*, I am drawn, *by objects*, away from the old humanism, away from contemporary man and ahead of him. I add to man the new qualities that I name.

That is what *Le Parti pris des choses* is.

Accounting for Words does the rest . . . But poetry as such doesn't interest me, in that what goes by the name of poetry these days is a crude analogical magma. Analogies are interesting, but less than differences. One must, by means of analogies, grasp the differential quality. When I say that the inside of a nut resembles a praline, it is interesting. But what is far more interesting is their difference. To make people experience analogies is one thing. Naming the differential quality of the nut: that's the goal, that's progress.

One must start from the *discovery* of Rimbaud and Lautréamont (concerning the necessity for a new rhetoric[4]).

And not from the *question* the first part of their works poses.

Up to now people have worked only from the question (or rather at restating the question more feebly).

---

4 Rimbaud: 'I now know how to salute beauty.' Lautréamont: *Les Poésies* (*passim*).

My sleep is fitful and disturbed.

My hands and feet are usually warm enough.

I have numbness in one or more regions of my skin.

A Minister can cure diseases by praying and putting his hand on your head.

I sometimes tease animals.

I am afraid of losing my mind.

Sometimes I am strongly affected by the personal articles of others such as shoes, gloves, etc., so that I want to handle or steal them though I have no use for them.

At times I feel like smashing things.

I have never felt better in my life than I do now.

I dream frequently about things that are best kept to myself.

I sweat very easily even on a cool day.

I do not blame a person for taking advantage of someone who lays himself open to it.

It makes me feel like a failure when I hear of the success of someone I know well.

I am embarrassed by dirty stories.

I try to remember good stories to pass them on to other people.

Someone has been trying to rob me.

I have had no difficulty starting or holding my urine.

I enjoy gambling for small stakes.

Statements from a psycho-diagnostic test developed in the USA in the 1940s. Subjects were asked to respond, true, false or cannot say.

I should like to belong to several clubs or lodges.

I like to talk about sex.

DAN O'BRIEN

The War Reporter Paul Watson: New Poems

The War Reporter Paul Watson Accuses the Poet

Good news about the sporadic interest
in your poems. But you'll have to retitle
this collection *The Forcibly Retired
War Reporter*. Because I can't persuade
bosses to let me go back to Syria
or even Kandahar. I keep chipping
away, but all they do is look past me
with eyes darting, as if half-expecting
Sirhan Sirhan. I don't know why, maybe
it's the insurance? Because the latest
hitch concerns so-called accidents. I asked,
Are death by crossfire and execution
both covered? No response yet. It's a cost
-benefit thing: Why do we need to go
now? And if we do go now how will we
find the extra hundred thousand dollars
needed to retrieve the beheaded corpse
of Watson? Given current financial
bellwethers. It's like trying to reason
one's way out of Hell. Not too long ago
bosses were fond of treacly platitudes
about The Need To Bear Witness. Bullshit
then, bullshit now. But excellent training
for Hollywood, right? Though I do wonder

if your poems are to blame. Because bosses
should never know you're human. Though I doubt
most editors even know how to read
poems. Ha ha ha. Which is why I'm spending
all my free time on my latest hobby,
mycology. It's taking much longer
than expected: misting, fanning, sniffing
obsessively. When you come visit me
on my island to write our TV script
together in my cabin, we'll trip balls
for inspiration. Then take a long hike
out past Murder Point. Where the First Nations
people threw off their colonial yoke,
for a time.

The War Reporter Paul Watson on the Really Real

My Chinese wife has some ancient wisdom
she'd like to secrete in our TV script
for bloggers in search of an Easter egg
in this Land of Illusion. *INT.*
– dark hallway in Beirut, reads the intro
to the character who's me, a haunted
yet handsome 50-something drudge cracking
the door on our Indian, hash-smoking
Buddhist therapist with a merciless
giggle and a few loose marbles. Karmic
about mental health, he doesn't believe
in Freud or SSRIs. And suicide's
so cliché. So he teaches acolytes
how to smoke the narghile pipe. Above
his rolling chair: gold characters dancing
balletically upon a battlefield

of silk incarnadine, the aforesaid
quotable which in loose translation reads:
The real is not real, just as the unreal
isn't really either.

The War Reporter Paul Watson Imagines His Character

feeling like a dead guest on a talk show
couch with more dead guests and a dead host who
entertain a studio audience
of the dead, all for the invisible
dead who watch at home. *But sometimes at night*
he'll still dream of life. With so many friends
gone – what could be the reason? His penance
is reporting, but redemption will come
from dropping out, giving up, whenever
he finds the courage.

The War Reporter and the Poet Fight

I sense we've depressed them, Dan. *Okay, Paul.*
This is Hollywood so they're expecting
the Bang Bang, Combat Sex. *I know.* Radio
has this saying: Listeners don't listen
because they're too busy doing dishes
or taking a shit. *Okay.* And by now
executives will be wondering if
their wives are shtupping the pool boys. Then what
would you change? You've got to follow the way
the distracted mind works. Okay. I hear
like this circular saw in that driveway

gnawing – ? Why don't we close the window then?
You're an actor onstage whose audience
will have stopped caring by now, Dan. I know
what an audience wants, Paul. Somebody
should kill somebody or – I'm not going to
do a tap dance for them. Okay. I won't
wear a lot of, I don't know, hats. Okay,
Dan, but still, you've got to *surprise* them! Let's
just try to get through this run-through once, Paul,
okay? Because I'm a good example
of somebody who can't pay attention
well. Ha ha ha. Ha ha ha. I feel that
your comments, Paul – Okay. About our pitch
have become kind of – What. Fear-based. They *are*
fear-based! Okay. My entire life is fear
-based, Dan! And my approach is to *ignore*
fear, Paul. Okay, but just be ready when
they get bored. The reason they'll get bored is
because we can't get through like two minutes
of this pitch without you stopping to give
me fucking notes! I may be wrong and if
I am well, sorry, but that reminds me
we need to inject more gallows humor
into this. Our task is to *focus* here,
Paul. Okay. Why don't we take a breather
and drink a glass of water, or maybe
something stronger? Oh, and also cut down
your intro, Dan. I'm just being myself,
Paul. Okay, but telling them you heard me
on the radio? What. Why don't you say
you had like this shotgun in your mouth and
I made you weep or something? You didn't
make me weep, though. What was the reason then
you first reached out to me? You know. Tell me
the reason. I've told you. But you've got to

move me, Dan! You've got to move me too, Paul!
Okay. And not go off on these tangents.
Okay. And you've got to keep track of time
because you don't have a very good sense
of time. I get that. And please stop talking
in like this shell-shocked monotone – I talk
in a monotone? You see this is what
I didn't want to do! But this is how
I talk, Dan! Okay. Why didn't you say
so before? Because I didn't want to
start a fight! But if you tell me today
I won't be boring tomorrow! I am
telling you now! Okay but I wasn't
getting it, Dan. Okay. I'm used to blunt
coworkers. I was exaggerating
because you pushed me. I need to be slapped
around, Dan. Paul, I feel like I'm getting
a lot of pressure here. No, no pressure
from me! What's important is that we try
to relax. Okay. And stop being scared
of scaring them. Okay. And that is why
you shouldn't be reading those how-to books
about Hollywood. You're right, I have been
in my head, Dan. You're scared. And I shouldn't
be reading that junk, it's junk! It's okay
if you're scared, I'm scared too. I've been searching
for answers. And all we can do is say
we have this story and do you want to
help us sell it? Okay, Dan. Okay, Paul.
Let's do this again. Okay. And this time
if I'm boring I want you to hit me
with the truth.

The War Reporter Paul Watson and the Week of Taking Meetings

In the beginning the Executive
says sorry she's late. Her kids pitched a fit
on the PCH en route to day camp
in Malibu. Like a dominatrix
flanked by bearded masochists. *Mad Men*-style
glasses in passive faces. I travelled
with the rebel side, says Paul. SCUD missiles
pulverizing apartment blocs. Digging
children out, mostly dead. I have some pics
if you'd like to see them. I can't even
begin to imagine! she cries. *Sorry
we're twenty minutes late.* A homely blonde
who seems somehow already jilted and
her fattish, whiskey-voiced, whiskered hipster
Number Two. Too many beards in the room!
japes the Poet. You're a poet? I am
so outclassed, winks Fat Beard. I went to grad
school for this? Sad Dumpy jokes. I forgot
to let my intern know what to order
for lunch, wait a sec. It's gallows humor,
says the War Reporter. If you enjoy
jokes-on-a-rope then you'll enjoy the world
of *The Zone*. Is that your tone? asks the Blonde
frowning. Sounds like a downer. Paul parries,
It's the new Rwanda! So everything
so far has been backstory? He might be
bisexual, concedes the Poet. If
you don't have an idea then don't act like
you do. The room seems to say. We don't know
what we don't know, do we? to paraphrase
Rumsfeld, Paul cracks wise. We're about to run
over, she says. Why don't we retire then
to the bar in the Cheesecake Factory?

suggests Paul. Wow, she says, just wow and thanks
for coming in! We have glimpsed the future
and they're stupid, murmurs Paul. But one day
they'll die too, soothes the Poet. *You* both *look
like war reporters!* glad-hands another
bearded young Turk. Horn-rimmed glasses. Congrats
on the Emmy, I say. Thank you but when
you get into business with a name like
Name Redacted – ! We're all feeling pretty
jazzed today. But the question is can we
do it all again? Which is where you jerks
come in. Ha ha ha. I've always been drawn
to villains, says Paul. Perhaps I'm jumping
the gun, says Mr Emmy. Your world's great
in terms of theme, and I get the soap
opera aspect here, but what's the story
of your Season One in just one word? Fish
-out-of-water, says the Poet. The truth
-teller-in-exile, the War Reporter
says at the same time. Thanks and a pleasure
to have met you! Well that went pretty well,
says Paul. Considering he's a man. *A voice
via speakerphone.* Bry's at Comic-Con
in San Diego. Say hi, Bry. Hello,
Carrie! Greetings, guys. Are you cosplaying
as something in particular? Carrie
sasses her absent colleague. There's a guy
in the corner, bearded, glasses. Pardon?
answers the Voice of Bry. That's funny, laughs
the Cornered Exec. War has eternal
appeal, explains Paul. That Somalian kid
sporting our corpse's goggles while flashing
my camera the finger? burnt flesh on sticks,
teeth in handkerchiefs? Speaking to the dead
soldier I said – sorry, I get choked up

just talking about it, still. His children
have children now. Okay, any questions
then, Bryan? she asks. The Beard smiles. Bry-Bry,
you still there? Sorry, I must've muted
my end, ha ha ha, ha ha ha, great job
everybody! That lady looked sleepy,
says Paul in the lobby. Probably got kids
to pick up in Malibu. *Mazel tov!*
says another Blonde Executive when
she learns my wife is pregnant. I adore
poems – promise! she crows. Reminding me of
a coxswain on the ladies' rowing team
I once wrote sonnets for. I'm so sorry,
says Paul, breaking down as he clicks open
The Picture on his iPad. I wear this
paracord bracelet in case I get stuck
in a jam, he says. You never know when
you might need a length of rope! I love no
I appreciate – I mean this has been
just fabulous! Standing up. We'll sit down
internally and discuss. A pleasure,
she smiles, and when's your baby due? Touching
wood. Ha ha ha! She cried! cries Paul. Real tears
pooled in her eyes! While the receptionist
validates our parking. Women tend to
cry more easily, thankfully. Going down,
he drones in the elevator. My shrink
works in this building, says the Poet. *Noon*
in some space-age solarium, two guys
with glasses, beards, like identical twins
who are secretly in love. Do we see
him kidnapped? beaten? tortured? Sure, says Paul.
Do you want to? I ask. Because there's nice
Arabs, and there's bad Arabs, Paul teaches.
The Zone's a morally ambiguous,

poisonous place. For instance, can we trust
who we're talking to right now? Will you kill
off any of our principal players?
they ask. Sure! says Paul. Would you like us to?
I ask. And is the idea that you two
would write this thing together? Sure! says Paul.
If you pay us to, I say. Well thank you
both for coming in. At the valet stand
in bleaching sun he says: I'm on the verge
of an actual breakdown. When they ask,
Does somebody get killed? – they get to slump
into their screening rooms. To be really
real, he adds, the character who should die
is the one we like the most. So, sushi?
inquires the Poet. Ha ha ha. Text me
if you can't find the place. *A conference call*
a lifetime later with the Fixer, half
-Indian, via Princeton, who dresses
in a Silver Lake sort of way, skinny
jeans and high tops, flannel and a blazer
without much structure, audibly stroking
his fulsome beard, amber, Ashkenazi
eyes, sea-green, Grandpa on the Jewish side
invented backyard pools so he knows how
to parlez-vous the patois where subtext
can be hard to hold on to – So the news
is everybody passed. Nobody cares
about war, really. And while your story's
heartbreaking, Paul, the truth is it simply
costs too much. But let's touch base down the line
and try and set up another brunch.

The War Reporter Paul Watson Walks the Ledo Road

It was the road some said couldn't be built
through Himalayan jungles in monsoons
less lethal than mosquitos, clouds of mites
nibbling like piranhas, leeches sneaking
life from thighs, scrotums, behind ears in pools
of sucking mud, vines like the embraces
of neurotic mothers, the bloody burst
of tigers from branches. Unseen jaguars
phantasmal like Africa. While the Japs
zapped brimstone from above. White officers
like antebellum slave-drivers grinding
their heels into black necks. All the while tires
swiveled down hopeless tracks, dragging more blacks
into the abyss. *I know we didn't*
sell our pitch, Paul. I'm sorry. But maybe
we could write it anyway? Evelio's
the son of black Cubans who rolled cigars
in Ybor City. In pictures his eyes
are mischievous. Garrison-capped. He joked
about poker, pretty girls and cuddling
tent-rats fatter than house cats. Weekend trips
into India for light bulbs, measuring
the road with a rusted surveying chain
for supervisors until he told them,
Jeeps have odometers, you know. Like me,
I tell Evelio, a professional
troublemaker. *I haven't heard from you*
in months. I hope you're safe. The baby is
here, and healthy. Her mother too. Maybe
we could write something entirely new
together? Like India, the Chinese are
resurrecting the road. Pounding concrete
cobbles into dirt. When the rains sweep through

the road swells, then shrinks like glass. In India
it's just a footpath. Whereas the Chinese
border's a bazaar, traders and tourists
on their way to transsexual burlesques
in Myanmar. In between villagers
promenade along Main Street. The tremor
of an approaching truck drives them onto
the verge, where they gawk at riders swaying
on benches, on buckets. *It's probably good*
we move on. Because you can't keep doing
what you do. And I can't either. We turn
to climb a hill to Hla Di Lu. Whose key
dangles from a necklace of gruesome twine
and unpops the padlock on her door where
somebody's spray-painted, Merry Xmas
and Happy New Year! Massaging memories
out of her brow. At her one table. Blurred
eyes like a newborn. The Japanese ran
her father through with bayonets. Mother
raped in this paddy. Whereas the black men
from America twisted fruit tins open
for her on the roadside. *I'm losing you,*
Paul. Your voice. Where are you now? In a room
in Oakland hardly bigger than the bed
that holds Evelio. Hands like mallets. Leg
amputated at the knee. His skin is
stretched canvas. Voice whispering. Every word
is hard labor. In 1943
he wrote, *We'll have to try and make the best*
of what trouble comes our way, till the day
we wake up from this nightmare. Close your eyes,
Evelio, the old road is coming back
to life. A strange light grows. As the alarm
rings our nurse into the neighboring room.

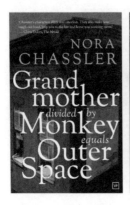 

ADNAN SARWAR

from You Don't Want to Die a Virgin

I had one friend in a coffin and another stood next to me on an airfield thousands of miles from home. The air smelt of war at night, and of heat and fuel. Some of us might not be coming back, our Commanding Officer had told us before we came out here, and it's a hard truth that people you laugh with, share tea with, dig a trench with, might not be there later. It happened when soldiers left the regiment, we didn't say it in these exact words but we missed them, we'd keep in touch but there was something missing and it was them in the next squadron photo. Life rumbles on giving us a stage for a bit. I thought these soldiers were everything and I loved them. I knew they had something in them and I felt it. I wanted to get to where they were but never had the reach, I didn't think I was ever good enough to be them, be with them, that they let me stand with them through their charity. What they had was more real than any God of mine. It was in front of me and it was something I could hold. It was a person wrapped in a camouflage suit. Where's your God now, Danny? My mouth opened and words became silence which I took back in and they whirled around my head whispering all the things I thought in the times when I didn't feel Him. There's nothing else. He's not there, is He? But don't say it Danny, no, don't say it because you don't want to upset people. You don't want the men to look at you funny and you don't want to speak your truth. But what does that make you? Does that make you tolerant, just letting things slide so we can all live in peace while you let it all creep on and on, or does it make you a coward? When you feel wrong inside and you don't say or do anything, when you let your body swallow it all, that sounds like cowardice. Was I a coward? How had I got into the military and how was I wearing a bomb disposal badge on my arm and how was I watching a dead friend being put on a plane in the war being this coward? Where's your God now they asked. He's not here in Kuwait and he wasn't there in Iraq, was he?

*

I'd be chased by white kids shouting 'Fucking Paki', threatening to kick my head in, the same lads I'd fight alongside when fighting other schools. There was a buzz as I ran on adrenaline. I didn't like the name calling and I didn't want my head kicked in but I didn't mind the running so much. You can get into a pace where it doesn't feel like you're making an effort, it's like you're flying and every foot stroke doesn't hit hard ground and your breathing at that rate is now normal. The wind you made would keep the sweat off and your mind was at rest, it was natural. I'd wish I had trainers on, school shoes were hard to run in, Dad wanted me to wear them so I looked smart but they made the knees hurt as I smacked through backstreets. On those days I'd get pushed around in the corridor and knew what was coming when the bell rang. On those days I was on my own and would learn lessons in life. I'd start running with a pack of lads but then some would break away from the front and then some would start jogging and then walking and covering their heads as the pack of white lads broke away too and the fastest of theirs caught the slowest of ours. I was never one of the fastest.

Wiry Pakistanis who did well on Sports Day would race off to safety but I wasn't the slowest either, not like the lumpy ones who ate too much and would probably get diabetes way before their time, they'd get picked off easily but only get a few smacks to the head and some spit in the hair and be left alone. They weren't worth more than that. The pack didn't feel satisfied if they hadn't earned their kill so they kept chasing. To be fat or fast was the key but I was a middle-of-the-road kind of guy. This was the way animals hunt other animals, I'd heard about it on the radio. That's what they were after, even if they didn't know it, they felt it, felt it in their beings that had grown through the years hunting, they wanted to strive just enough to feel like they'd earned the kill and that kill was me. I was striving and my efforts were honest, my legs and lungs were hurting, I was going to tire and in my tiring I was going to be an easy win, they would have worked just hard enough and I would be just tired enough, life has a funny way of ranking you.

This middle-of-the-road gazelle would taste good. I was good meat. Where I lacked the legs, I learnt how to use my brain. I used tricks and hid in back gardens but one day they caught me behind Michelle's house. A back street. They'd come in from both ends, they'd been smart and used their heads and the law of the jungle meant they'd earned me. There was no escape, I couldn't fly so I had to fight. They closed in and I accepted my fate. Let's do it then. I'd been here before and the pain doesn't last for ever. There was no point losing too quickly because they'd realise they'd been had and kick you more, there was no point trying any tricks, there was only that one thing to do and that was fight as best as you could. With everything you had. With your fists into someone's head. Hitting their skull with your knuckles and taking the pain and doing it again and again. You can try all you want to to tell a different story and to rewrite your own history but all along the way you've been seen and witnessed in arenas surrounded by others. You've been seen, judged and ranked.

Here today I was going to get my head kicked in and that was going to be part of my history, part of me. Come on, then. White faces all around shouting and spitting and me in the middle. There was no point in pretending. There was only fighting. Come on, then. And there was a sliver of a thing, a beautiful thing really, it might be called hope, it might be called spirit, whatever it was, it let you believe that all was not lost. Yes you were surrounded by the enemy, and no they weren't going to let you leave until you bled, but you might, you just might win. So let's do it. You might just win. It was always a boy I hadn't fought before. It was a system to see who the Cock of the School was, who the hardest boy was, the best fighter. It was how lads at Towneley busied themselves in between fighting other schools, how they kept themselves sharp, how they ranked themselves and it impressed the girls if you were Cock of your class or year or the school. Sometimes the girls came to watch. I didn't want Michelle to ever see me in the ring or Kim or Debbie or Sam because they were her friends. I called the lad I fought a 'Honky' as many times as he called me a 'Paki' but mostly we swung fists at each other, it was hard to keep up a conversation. Just before the fight we'd start bouncing, I don't know why but both of us would buoy up and down a little as we moved in to the fight. Others helped by pushing us and then we'd scrap like dogs, teeth and fists clenched, minutes became long painful hours. Bang. There was no point going for the stomach, the face would win it for you or grabbing the back of the neck with your hands and kneeing the victim in the face – that was a show stopper. It hurts, getting kneed in the face.

There's the hard knee with a thin layer of skin, hair and school trouser and there's my face with all its soft bits. My eyes which would be pressed in and bruise and blacken, my forehead might hurt his knee but it would hurt me more, my nose would gush, my lips would burst, my teeth would loosen, my chin would make me bite my tongue, if I turned my head or he did he'd knee my ears which would ring, and there's the bit under my ear where my jaw meets it that would stun me with a numbness if he kneed me there. Going for the head would win it for you. A stomach is nothing, a back, legs, arms? No, the head. That's the one thing to go for. And that's what the boy did to me behind Michelle's house. The next day we'd dissect this fight and the lads would tell me what I should have done but they're not here now. I went for him. My punches didn't land. All the shouting was for him, they told him to kill me, to do me, to fuck me up – knock me out. He dragged my jumper over my head and kneed me in the face and I felt my nose bang and go warm with the blood and go numb on his knee and my legs gave way with my spirit and I fell.

Too easy. He kicked me a few more times before they dragged him away laughing. I'd lost and got off the floor kicking and scraping on broken milk bottles pulling that stupid jumper off wanting to throw it away but I knew we were poor. Some of the white lads stayed and helped me up saying it hadn't been a fair fight because of the jumper. Ha. I walked home with my head ringing, wiping my bloody face on my shirt. I was glad to not have seen any of the girls and on my way home I went past the tyre garage and they asked me if I was all right and I said of course I was, they should see the other guy. Good lad, they said, don't let them beat you. I fucking won't, I said. Past the tyre garage comes the main town centre but if you walk along the canal you can avoid all the other people asking if you're all right because you are really. The pain doesn't last for ever. It's just growing up. Wipe your face, shake yourself off, you've just been ranked, at least you know where you belong now.

Up on the canal you could see parts of Burnley you couldn't from the streets. There were old bridges and trees and it ran though parks, it was a different Burnley. It was quiet. I smiled and laughed on the way home, I was never going to be Cock of the School, Cock of the Year, Cock of anything, I was a middle-of-the-road guy. Sorry, Michelle. I got home and the blood, sweat and fear had dried. I'd sneak upstairs and wash my face and hide my shirts.

But then I learnt how to fight, how to bluff my way in and scare the other lad before we'd started and these were the days that I'd win and they'd leave me alone, carrying my victim away. I got faster and stronger but a little too late. Those days I'd wish you were there, Michelle, I would have won you then, banging a lad's head around a back street. But by then you'd grown breasts and I used to stare at you in class, you'd straightened your hair and tied it back into a bun with a little fringe and you looked great in a tight white shirt.

*

I was a twenty-five-year-old man, not a child but finally a man. I was dressed in a green camouflage uniform which was going to catch the eye of any enemy soldier, not that I thought them my enemies, just other actors. I had short black hair and brown eyes and dog tags around my neck which gave my name and number and my religion and they felt warm in the sun on my chest and salty from the sweat when I ran the chain through my mouth. If the mortars had gotten me and not just made me pieces of flesh and smashed bone that somebody would have to weigh out up to twelve stone along with some sand to fill the locked coffin, then they might have found my body intact with those warm, sweaty dog tags around my neck and they would have said 'Muslim, this one', and made sure I got the right burial. Muslim? Yep, that's what was stamped on his dog tags, must have been a Muslim. The guy with me was shouting. Me? I wasn't thinking, just ticking along on fumes. But I was getting there. I was getting to the point where it all fell into place.

When all the blocks came together and built something and then fell away because the floor they stood on wasn't there. Twenty-five years old doesn't matter. It's a lot of years in a life but not a lot in the whole game. Why not spend your last days here? Identity didn't matter. Brown skin? That didn't matter. Muslim doesn't matter, that's just where I was born and to who. My black hair, brown eyes, two legs and two arms don't matter. Six foot, twelve stone and trim doesn't matter, forty-inch chest, scar on left wrist, little finger on right hand broken on somebody's head doesn't matter, my account means nothing because I am no one. Nothing matters. The mortar doesn't matter, the air that can't stop it matters only a little more, it'll still be here when we're done and gone. Breathing it in doesn't matter. I don't need to exist, I don't need to be here. It only matters if you pretend to care. But at least that realisation came. I was nothing.

I was one in over six billion and metal was raining on me and I could just disappear and eventually even that wouldn't matter any more. My body could have any burial you wanted it to, it wouldn't matter to me. Bury me, burn me, laugh about me dying a virgin, raise a glass for all the drink I never had – here lies Danny Sarwar, the idiot. You fucking idiot, we tried with you, we tried to make you see. We'll have a drink for you. But it was nice to be around, not that I would have had that thought if I didn't exist so maybe being around was something I should be grateful for, that I could think these things and feel this thing between me and family and soldiers and friends and this girl with me. Everyone we meet, everything we do makes a link but the more links you make the harder it feels when you break them when you die so it's easier to break them sooner. Die early or don't make links. Some links can't be broken and they reach like long arms though time to you, you're always some mum's son. Bomb me more, you fuckers.

*

Luke dying was a full stop. Full stops say that's the end. The end of my point or the end of it all. But then it can carry on. It goes on. And on . . . see? I like them, these infinite circles into which if they do stop something, you can jump and go somewhere else through the black tunnel and end up on another page, in another part of the story or somewhere else altogether. Luke went on like that. I knew him a short while but he changed me forever. I don't want to come back this way. I jumped into him and haven't stopped travelling in that full stop of his and here she is giggling at me. Outside is the parade square and it's surrounded by grass, on part of the grass is a sandy coloured Iraqi tank that wasn't there before 2003, we saw it after we thought we'd won the war and brought it back with us to sit there, on our parade square, our Iraqi tank. This was my first time. It had taken Luke and Iraq and Biscuits and it had taken full stops and commas and other false starts. They'd taken me to the edge and shown me how to jump off it into new things and fill parts of my head that had never been awake before. I don't believe in you, God. I want to jump.

She looks into the box. Inside is a diary I wrote every day I was in the war from Kuwait to Iraq and back home, and there are letters people sent, some from my brothers telling me what Mum says, why didn't I know you then? I'd love for these letters to be from you. I'd love a letter to say you were thinking about me because I was always thinking about you, I've been making dreams about you for so long. You're the girl who should have been before. I wasn't as brave then, I'm not that brave now but I'm trying, you being here is making me like that. There are some letters in there from other girls, I pull them from her, they're not important – you are. Life's not perfect but if it was these notes would have been from you. Just girls who wanted to write to a soldier on the front line and all they got was me being bombed and not knowing what to say. Others knew. They wrote back stories of heroes and bullets and sand, stories of heat and bodies – stories of Iraq. This war, this boring and mundane war, this war where people would sit safely miles away using joysticks to kill the enemy, this war that would never live up to expectations of soldiers who were trained to kill, was going to make liars out of some of us. And some of those liars lied and girls laid on their backs for them when they came back and that's the truth. They slept with those girls who wrote to 'A Soldier, Op Telic, Iraq'.

I kept them, yeah, but only because they gave me a little power but I didn't need them after I met you. One letter I never got back was my Last Letter. We wrote those in case we died and our families would get our last thoughts, last words, apologies and promises that we were happy always and you shouldn't cry for us. Don't worry. We lived our dreams. We burnt those letters before leaving. She opens the diary. It's personal but it's her so it's all right. And she reads. You've got nice handwriting. It's okay, I wish it was better, Dad bought me a nice pen when I started school and he told me people judge you on your writing so he signs his name carefully, takes his time, making each letter clear and rounded and nice looking. Well, I like it just like this. I shrug which says it's okay but what I mean is thank you, thank you for thinking something good of me. See the reason the handwriting's not that good is I wrote it mostly in the back of a Land Rover at night, wearing a little red head-torch with the door closed because we had to keep strict light discipline. Red's better because it's soft, white can cut so much into a night.

Once I'd finished writing up the day, I'd ease the handle quietly, push open the door with clenched teeth and go outside to breathe the cool night's desert air. The land was vast, I didn't know what that word meant before I saw their desert, it was vast, they said it went as far as the eye could see but it went further. It was like we had taken everything we had and laid it flat in front of us. I'd raise my rifle sight to my eye and all I could see was beauty. I knew then that I was one of the lucky ones. The breeze would run its fingers along me. It had everything, it had a taste, a sound, a smell, a picture and a feeling. I never wanted to be anywhere else, and I've only felt like that a few times. I feel like that now, I feel like that when I'm in Mum's arms, I feel like that when Dad's smiling because he's proud of me, I feel like that with you but I don't know how to put it into words, I want to feel like that for ever but I know it's a special feeling and has to be rationed, when I get it, I can go for miles on that little bit.

They've got a beautiful country, we made holes in it but go and stand there in the early chill of the night and look at that sky, you can write anything in it, if you want life's meaning you might find it there. You wrote this every day? Every day I could, in the back of Land Rovers after my day was done, I didn't know why I was writing it, maybe it was for you, for now, so you can look at it and think things of me. Think more of me. I wrote what happened to me. I like it she says, and puts it back, my war diary, in the box on top of the letters, the photos and the Iraqi flag with God is Great written in Arabic in between its green stars. You do love them don't you, she says more than she asks. Yeah, I do. Don't you love me? You're running along on your own because you've just worked out how, when you were growing up, Mum was there – she still is but she needed to be there more back then – but now you're on your own. And you're running. Dad's proud of you, you're doing it, you're riding a bike, you've got nice handwriting people comment on, you get good marks in exams, people smile when you're around, you're making it. Dad's smiling one of those hard-won smiles. Mum wants you to still be home but Dad says it's a good thing you're doing, stand up for yourself, son. So you stand and you run, and your legs are strong, your lungs can pull in so much air and you're running, you're sure about everything, if there are problems along the way you'll solve them straight away with ease, you are strong, you will fight, they will go down, you're running on your own and the path is long and the sides are blurred but then you see a face and you slow – slow – slow until you stop and need to go another way, it's the way she's making for me. It's her face. Don't you love me she asks. I nod my head and a warm pulse inside lets me know it wants to be part of this moment. Yes, I love you.

I wish this diary had been about you. About moments with you. She kisses me with strawberry lips. I don't know the rules for when you say I love you, I just say it when I feel I do and I feel it for her, feel it now. You're supposed to be cool and this and that but with her I can be me and she thinks that's cool. Love comes, and it starts with Mum, then Dad, then friends, then the soldiers and now her, it's all around and it just keeps coming, it doesn't need to stop because it never fills me, there's always room for more, to me and from me. I know I can love for ever and I want to. Won't you say you love me too? She just smiles. I grab her and she laughs. Stop keeping secrets from me, say you love me too. I don't know if she knows what she's doing either but she knows more than me so I'll follow her and try and get to somewhere new. She takes off her jacket.

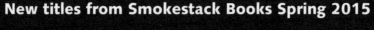

ANDREW ELLIOTT

Fourteen Poems

Doppelgänger

I once took my parents for lunch in a very expensive restaurant.
Dining at the table next to ours was Lucian Freud with a girl.
To begin with he stared at my mother who was even then
more beautiful than anyone else in the restaurant,
including the American actress at whom I made a point of *not* staring.

Then he turned his gaze on my father who in terms self-obsession
could have taken Lucian Freud to the cleaners, passed him over,
taken his ticket, and come back the next day to collect him
like a camel's-hair coat in cellophane. I felt for the girl
who was struggling. I could see she could see what was happening.

When our eyes met I winked and she laughed. She rolled
her eyes and I nodded. She had the kind of eyes which if eyes
were to be put into mass production would stream out of factories
in South Korea, and come in a choice of colours . . . My mother
for whom the meal was a treat was interested only in the actress.

My father was complaining as he always does about the food
to a waiter of skin and bone who may have been an artist himself,
starving for his art in a garret, only waiting to make ends meet,
the sparks to suddenly fly. I thought, *Him and that girl*
should get together. She's thin like him. They'd be happy and be able

to survive like freegans on what people like my father sent back . . .
Having already scraped his vegetables carefully onto a plate
on the side, my father was picking at his fish like a surgeon
trying to cut out a cancer. I thought of what all this was costing,
how children's eyes get everywhere, dragging their minds behind them.

Meanwhile Freud had continued to stare and the novelty of someone
so famous staring at my father had worn off. It was embarrassing.
I'd a pea all ready on my fork to flick but when next I looked
their table had been cleared. The waiter was spreading a clean white cloth,
tugging it tight to the edges. With her eyes as much as anything else

my mother flashed, *She's leaving!* My father wanted pudding.

Fathers and Sons

In the decades after WW2 German history was a brown field site
and architects found themselves in demand. None more so
than Paul Schneider-Esleben – whose son, the musical Florian,
would later find not fame exactly but the satisfaction
of a job well done, delivered in time like a washing machine,
with the influential Kraftwerk – for whom it had been the golden age

which stands in marked contrast to the history of postwar Britain
where famously Mick Jagger could get *no* satisfaction
despite the time and effort he put into it, the lips, the hips, the legacy
of his father's physical discipline seeing him at an age
when for most men the pension comes in handy enough
still out there putting food on the table as if age had not wearied him.

The Rise and Fall of the English Novel

On the one hand industry as it would have been then –
massive, infernal, consisting of hundreds of thousands of men
who despite being made ill by the filthy, dark, often dangerous conditions,
shovelled the coal, worked the machines, lent their shoulders to whatever
       the wheel.

On the other hand this: a daisy chain, the last thing a woman would be
       wearing
were she to have taken off the little she began with, the floral frock
which she can see hanging from the branch of a tree, adding
to the apples such additional weight as the branch would appear to be able
       to take.

The Storm in American Fiction

Without necessarily stopping she'll look up from what she is doing
and see across the bedroom wall, falling slower
than she'd have thought a thing could fall,
the shadow, made by the moon, of a maple leaf blown
from the tree before being swept across the floor and vanishing

under the bed like something belonging to her husband
– whose tongue is in her cunt, whose cock is in her mouth –
the loss of which will drive him to turn upside down the house
like the wind may yet the tree and drive away their children
if it weren't for whom she'd have left him and gone to find herself.

Modernism

I had pitched up in Mexico and thought to visit my old friend Bill
whose seemingly insubstantial house, projecting from the side
of a massive, green, quite misty mountain can be seen from the valley –
especially in the morning when the sun turns pink its picture window –

to be like something which the men, the women, their little children
who are already out here working the fields, could never have expected
to have seen in their lifetime, the children who've been up there reporting
a construction unsupported by stanchions but protruding directly

from out of the rocks like something has driven it clean through the
    mountain,
only stopping when on emerging, quite arbitrarily, it found itself looking
out over their valley, just as – like Janus – it must look over the next
where people (not dissimilar to themselves) will look up in the evening

and see the sun as it sets reflect, a slightly deeper pink perhaps,
and think as they make their way home from the fields, following
in the footsteps of their numinous ancestors – that were they to look back
upon reaching their homes, stooping to steer through the narrow black
    doors

the littlest child as they would do a hen, the house would be giving off
a light of its own, so unlike anything they have known that the candles
they live by would once lit appear forlorn, writhing on their wicks
like the hands of priests in the face of a persuasive atheistic modernism

with its access to capital, just as more primitive priests before them
would have stood in despair, attempting to combine with all that they knew
that brutal intrusion, that glittering conquistador . . . Was Bill that figure
I could see sipping a Scotch, with Louise his fifth and final wife? Louise

about whom there would later be doubts and, following Bill's untimely
death, accusations which I was quick to dismiss, refusing to take seriously
any such thoughts – knowing Louise to be self-possessed, sure – of her
being a cold and calculating lesbian who'd made Bill beg in the bedroom.

From the Danish

Two middle-aged women in bed, already only partially clothed.
Outside there is sky, a beach, the former grey, the latter white, the grass
a combination of the two which may help us to see how the women
are struggling in themselves to combine not only the whites of their bodies
but the greys of their stormy hair until out there it begins to grow dark,

the dark bringing with it the lights of container ships passing on the
       horizon,
a Maersk Line, for example, bound for the port of New York, however
many thousand tons of steel being steered down the old whale road
by a good man, the son of his father, who feels a great swelling of pride
when he sees in the eyes of his crew in what high regard they hold him.

Martians,

had they ever materialized, would have appeared
to such people as saw them to be thin-limbed
and physically enfeebled because of the thinness
of the atmosphere in which they had come into being

and might have walked something like a man
who passed me all those years ago on MacDougal
where I liked to pass an hour every morning
with a coffee, a croissant, an American classic –

a *Moby-Dick*, an *Invisible Man* – from which
I'd occasionally break off for a sip or to lick
the tip of my index finger and pick up such flakes
of golden croissant as remained, translucent,

not only on my plate but on the top of a table
that could have been oak, the front of my T-shirt,
my blue-jeaned lap, and then ferry them to my tongue
like you sometimes see men pick flakes of tobacco

in old documentaries about this lost world or that . . .
On this one occasion when I looked up I saw a man
who appeared to be vanishing, even as I stared –
as I'd stared ten years earlier at a black man

whose appearance in our town out of nowhere
had seen my dad ring my mum to come quickly –
but who had just enough strength left to smile
and was gone before reaching the corner.

Germany?

No, but somewhere quite like it, little further east,
a minor town, a trading post, regionally famous
for the quantities of red tape its officials hold
at their disposal and the fog in which every street ends

inconclusively, often when a cat crosses your path
or a nervous dog – nervous about what? –
a pig, a horse, the odd rhinoceros after which
each street comes to be named, in your own mind at least.

I say town but its population of Germans alone
is approximately equivalent to the number of Germans
who would have been living in London in 1848
and when you think of all the other ethnic groups

packed into tenements, a testament to their builder,
you have to laugh at the quaintness of that
as you would upon innocently opening a cupboard,
expecting, at worst, a pair of cockroaches, a Mr and a Mrs,

only to find a boy or a girl squeezed in there,
their faces so contorted that you don't at first realize
what they're doing to themselves. When you do
you close the door immediately and climb back down

the ladder that allowed you to get access in the first place.
The child's grandmother is a friend of yours –
together you go way, way back. From time to time
she'll ask if you could spare her a little red tape.

What's a little tape between friends? Isn't tape
what we're regionally famous for? That and the fog
in which every street ends with you walking away
having clocked off with a roll as requested in your briefcase.

The Other House

In this, the most Bergmanesque of all my poems to date,
I would like to begin with the boat that has taken us out
to the island and the man to whom the boat belongs
who fails to wave as he vanishes, rowing back into the mist.

There is one other house on the island but the owners
have locked it up, and will only come back in the spring.
Knowing so little about me I understand that you'll be
anxious to begin with. The island is fine, but not so large

and I know it so much better than you do. The house is
simply furnished, there are lamps and a wood-burning stove,
but it too is not so large. The days themselves are short
and you can walk around the island in the hour which

you are free to stretch as long as the light lasts, standing
on the last rock out there, failing to look over your shoulder
when I shout from the house about dinner, some platter
I've foraged myself – goosefoot, samphire, white asparagus.

Perhaps if there was a sex scene, a candle carried into
your bedroom or there on the rug at the stove. Could there
be a better reason to have come here where no one can hear
you scream? Or even a scene where you strip and wade

into the grey-green water, standing like you did on the rock.
What reason could there be not to swim home? Am I so big
an ogre that I'd do all I could to prevent you? Aware of
being watched, you don't. *He has seen me*, you think. *It's over.*

Two Questions

I was ten when they rounded up the witches
and drove them through the streets at pike point.
In the square they put them in a pen like sheep,
made them strip and then left them like that.
They turned their backs on the people of the town
who by now had gathered round the pen three deep.
The younger ones did what they could for the old.
I remember their backs being yellow with sputum
and the blood which in those days was common in sputum
before someone sent for the grey, carbolic smocks
of whose hems the flames weren't slow to take hold
when, several nights later, no longer like women,
having had their heads shaved, they were tied to stakes.
Is the world a better place for having once been bad?

I'm fifty now. All that horror has been long forgotten,
closed like a book, those who did it dead or doting.
I live alone. I never married. I have no children
which isn't to say I've never known a woman
nor ever had an inkling of what people call Love.
The town has done well, grown in my lifetime into a city . . .
Old school friends never fail to stop when they see me.
Asked where I'm living, I roll my eyes as if to say,
*You see that window, way up there, it keeps me fit
and it costs next to nothing.* Then I make my excuses . . .
Once, when I was fourteen, a girl gave me an apple
and when I ate it completely – the seeds, the stalk –
she bit her lip and frowned, said her name was Isentrud . . .
Whenever you think of her now do you feel inconsolably sad?

My Novel

begins in Las Vegas but then – for reasons that need not detain us –
quickly puts Las Vegas behind it like Man's unquenchable thirst
for riches blazing in the sky now the sun has set for the first
however many pages it takes for the novel to bury it like a crime

and find itself driving through the desert where it sees what
looks like an ordinary family – the father out front with his briefcase,
the wife in whose arms their youngest is sleeping, their eldest,
bringing up the rear, already hanging over them like a scorpion's tail –

walking with only a chicken wire-fence between them and the Nevada Test
      Site.
The novel pulls over and rolls down the window. The woman is clearly
exhausted and is only too glad to accept. For the next five pages
or more the novel crawls along at a snail's pace as she tries to persuade

her husband. *Bob*, she pleads, *please! For the children* . . . Their eldest,
having slipped in beside her just sits there feigning disinterest, as if to say,
Me? In a novel? How lame . . . until the man pulls a gun from his briefcase
and, climbing in, threatens, *No funny stuff, y'hear? Or I'll kill ya.*

Over the course of the dusty pages that follow the novel gets to know
the family well. It loves their youngest who is funny; feels for the eldest
who has issues; falls hopelessly for their mother who is wonderful
while keeping an open mind on the man who may or may not be insane.

Only slowly does it dawn that the novel – the novel, not the family –
is dying and that the family has been a kind of red herring that will end
in what looks like a huddle outside the door of so nice an old house
that the novel will draw out its departure like time running out in its rear

view until the eldest looks over her shoulder and smiles despite her braces.

Something Unnaturally Fast

Once in a bar in New Orleans
the corner of my eye was caught
by something unnaturally fast
running up the wall to my right.

It was hot, such hot nights happen
and there's not an awful lot
you can do about it. A dark bar,
candles, music, I was sitting there

sipping a cold beer when up the wall
this thing nearly had me jump out
of my skin. To this day I don't know
what it was but, given how the woman

to whom I'd been talking saw nothing
but the shock on my face, there's
the theory she was quick to advance
that it must have been something

I imagined. *You imagine so much*,
she said. *Maybe later you'll imagine* . . .
She smiled, let it drop and said, *Anyways* . . .
We'd been talking about art, about Dubuffet . . .

She looked like Brecht in his heyday –
the hair – back, sides and front –
the same little glittering glasses . . .
Was she a Fellow at Tulane University?

I can tell that you're nervous. Don't be.
Then, leaning in a little bit closer,
Can I trust you to keep me a secret?
When I tell you what to do, don't quibble.

A girl like me doesn't come often.
There are only so many of us left . . .
I can tell you're a little bit squeamish . . .
You can trust me! she said, *I'm an anarchist!*

When she bent to her strawberry daiquiri
the straw turned red like a vein
and I thought of that thing on the wall,
how big it had been and how fast.

The candlelight crackled on her glasses.
A shiver ran down my spine.
I thought of how some things resist
by taking all the weight you can put on them.

Sorrow

I once took a friend to Auschwitz.
He could drive. I couldn't.
It was him took me in that sense.

I remember us standing at the gate.
Work will set you free, it said.
We looked at each other and laughed.

We'd never done a day in our life.
We're doomed, I said as we stood there
like the lines in a Wundt illusion.

We'd come unprepared for the cold –
I in my best Hawaiian shirt,
you in a rib-hugging sweater in beige

that stopped so far short of your wrists
it looked like you'd rolled your sleeves up
and meant if not work then business.

Still, we persevered. Or I did.
I've come all this way, I reasoned.
I could feel you hanging on my shoulder

stopping to look at what I looked at.
It was as if I'd been issued with my own
uniquely numbered ghost like one of those machines

you can hire in museums to enhance
the experience and yet all I was getting
was *Breath, breathing, difficulty with . . .*

Call it what you will it was giving me
the creeps. I ran out of patience.
I said, *Go and look at something of your own*

for once. Go on. Fuck off. I suppose
you could say that I snapped. *Look*, I said,
I'm sorry. Y'hear me? I said I'm sorry.

To which you replied, *Can we go now?*
I rolled my eyes, I thought, *What's the point?*
You can take a horse to water . . .

Back in the car we put on the heater.
I said, *It's a pity we're straight.*
If we weren't we could kiss and make up.

And at that we laughed for the first time
since we'd stood at those famous old gates
like the lines in a Wundt illusion.

Life

I am sipping my coffee in a diner in the South.
I am watching the reflection of the waitress
in the glass. A woman in her mid to late forties,
her beauty shines like a ghost in the darkness
of a street where the stores are boarded up
as if in preparation for a hurricane. Were a bus –
destination: *Los Angeles* – to stop outside the diner
and her reflection to look over its shoulder,
smile at me as if to say, *I'm old enough*
to be your mother . . . before joining those waiting
to board the bus then take a seat towards
the back, the bus being as full as the diner is empty
with people intent on a new life out west, I might
be moved to leave my coffee, dash from the diner,
board the bus, take the seat beside her reflection
and watch, as the bus begins to vibrate, how she moves
from one middle-aged man to another, offering
to each so steamy a refill that their red necks rise
into their faces until finally I see her come to me
(craning my neck as the bus pulls out), tossing back
her hair, cocking her head like she's weighing me up,
asking (being friendly), *Where ya from? Where ya*
headed? – difficult questions that leave me tongue-tied –
then telling me the motel I've checked into has bugs . . .
It's as if she's thinking, *Why'd he be headed for LA*
if not stardom? I don't think he's . . . I think
I'll go with him . . . And so sitting down and telling me
the story of her life. How when she was but a little
girl a big star had been what she'd wanted to be
and how she still had a reel of old film her daddy took
of her running around in their back yard with wings on –
You can tell how it's summer and the sun hasn't set yet . . .
But then a boy recorded me doin' a thing once,

said it had been nice of me to do it at the time. Then,
him bein' a boy who knew how to do stuff, he copied
the video and made it available at a reasonable price.
It was as if I had suddenly made a name for myself,
and when my daddy got a wind of it he went berserk,
stormed out of the house with his hunting rifle,
shot the boy who lived next door, blew his head off
by all accounts but in his anger, gotten confused,
shot the wrong boy and would've been sentenced
to death by the judge if I hadn't been twelve years old
at the time and told by my mama to sit there blubbin'
like I was truly contrite for the evil I had done
which meant he got life without parole . . . After that,
the girls that she had known? She could see them look at her
and think, *There but for the grace of God* . . . with a far-
away look in their eyes like Jesus was their Lord
and saviour and had taken his punishment
like a real man . . . The bus by now having turned the corner.

Forward Arts Foundation

We celebrate excellence in poetry and bring it to the widest possible audiences through
The Forward Prizes for Poetry
The Forward Books of Poetry
National Poetry Day
and other innovative, collaborative and inventive programmes

**Forward
Prizes
for Poetry**

To learn of our initiatives, sign up at
www.forwardartsfoundation.org
or contact us at Somerset House,
Strand, London WC2R 1LA
020 7845 4655
Registered charity number 1037939

DAVID COLLARD

Moby Dick's Hyphen

The opening line of Melville's novel is not 'Call me Ishmael'. This appears only after fifty pages of what the author calls 'Front Matter', an accumulation of fragments like the unsightly trash and clutter surrounding a whaling station, rough chunks of text roughly flensed from the body of leviathan literature. We have to pick our way carefully through these gobbets of cetacean lore before we arrive at that celebrated salutation. But those impatient readers who skip straight to Ishmael, or who cut to the chase at the first sighting of the white whale in Chapter 133, will miss a mesmerising compendium of 'higgledy-piggledy whale statements' encompassing science, philosophy, metaphysical speculation, poetry and folk-tales, with passages from the Bible, Pliny, Plutarch, Montaigne, Rabelais, Hobbes, Bunyan, Milton – and that's just the first three pages.

The novel's actual first words are:

ETYMOLOGY
(Supplied by a late consumptive usher to a grammar school)

There follows a deflationary introduc-tion by Melville himself, mocking the imaginary compiler as a 'mere painstak-ing burrower and grubworm of a poor devil of a Sub-Sub'. This is all great fun, but the editors behind my Kindle ver-sion have, quite understandably, moved all this 'Front Matter' to an appendix, realising that it's unlikely to hook the first-time reader who may feel they've downloaded another book entirely. But Melville certainly knew what he was doing, and what he was doing was something very modern, very strange and, it seems to me, in danger of being lost in this era of ebooks and indifferent editing. We'll come back to this meta-textual issue later. My first concern is an apparently trivial matter, but one that has bothered me for years and might be added to the clutter of Front Matter sur-rounding the novel: why is *Moby-Dick* hyphenated?

Approaching the issue by way of a digression – a very Melvillian strategy – we might recall Lewis Carroll's *Through the Looking-glass* and Alice's forest en-counter with the kindly White Knight, who offers to sing to her and adds, by way of clarification: '[t]he name of the song is called "Haddocks' Eyes".'

'Oh, that's the name of the song, is it?' Alice said, trying to feel interested.

'No, you don't understand,' the Knight said, looking a little vexed. 'That's what the name is *called*. The name really *is* "The Aged, Aged Man."'

'Then I ought to have said "That's what the song is called"?' Alice corrected herself.

'No, you oughtn't: that's another thing. The song is called "Ways and Means" but that's only what it's *called*, you know!'

We later discover the song really *is* 'A-sitting on a Gate', although the tune, needless to say, is another matter. Simply put, the hyphenated (and conventionally italicised) *Moby-Dick* is a book, or rather the title of a book; but the unhyphenated Moby Dick isn't a book at all, in the same sense that Elizabeth Bennett and Leopold Bloom aren't books. Moby Dick is the name of a whale in a book called *Moby-Dick*. *Moby-Dick*, not Moby Dick, is a book although *Moby-Dick* is not really the title of the book in which Moby Dick appears but, as the White Knight would say, is only what the name of the book is called.

The *real* name of the book, or at least the title under which the book first appeared in America in November 1851, is *Moby-Dick; or The Whale*. In the publisher's double spaced upper case it creates a more powerful impression as **MOBY-DICK; OR, THE WHALE**, the punctuation marks like Nantucket hooks and lances embedded in the pale flank of the title-page. That semi-colon

is working hard, though not as hard as what one excitable literary blogger has declared 'the greatest hyphen in American letters'. (What are the others? Kurt Vonnegut's *Slaughterhouse-Five* and Joseph Heller's *Catch-22* come first to mind, although in both cases the hyphen merely proposes a bureaucratic continuum of other Slaughterhouses, other Catches.) What the hyphen does to Moby Dick in *Moby-Dick* is unclear, not least because 'Dick' is not a number, not a Five or a 22, not part of any stable series, not even a suffix. But then 'Moby' isn't a prefix, as we shall see.

To muddy matters further the *first* first edition, which had appeared in three volumes in Britain a month earlier, was called simply *The Whale* (or, to be precise, **THE WHALE**). In what may be the editorial gaffe of the century Melville's Epilogue, in which Ishmael survives the climactic destruction and sinking of the *Pequod*, was dropped by the British publishers and the London critics pounced gleefully on the omission, pillorying the author for killing off his narrator and thus retrospectively sabotaging the entire enterprise. The critics were united in their derision: 'so much trash belonging to the worst school of Bedlam literature'; 'wantonly eccentric; outrageously bombastic'; 'bad rhetoric, involved syntax, stilted sentiment and incoherent English'; 'Mr Melville's Quakers are the wretchedest dolts and drivellers, and his Mad Captain [. . .] is a monstrous bore'. American reviewers, faced with the complete text in one volume – this time including the Epilogue – tended nevertheless to follow the British critics' lead and were, if anything, even harsher.

Melville at the age of thirty-two now had a promising future behind him and his literary career went into a steep decline. His astonishing short story *Bartleby the Scrivener* appeared anonymously in 1853, and the eponymous copy clerk's melancholic inertia can be read as a parable of the author's dilemma. Two decades of remunerative boredom were to follow when Melville took up a post as a New York City customs officer, a distraction being a visit to the Holy Land and the composition of an unreadable 16,000-line epic poem *Clarel*. His other masterpiece *Billy Budd* remained unpublished for over thirty years after the author's death at the age of seventy-two. His passing went largely unremarked, although the *New York Times* obituary notice (29 September 1891) referred in passing to a book called *Mobie Dick* [*sic*]. A revival of interest in *Moby-Dick* had to wait until the 1920s when a new readership began to develop. D. H. Lawrence, an early champion, wrote in 1923: 'it is a great book, a very great book, the greatest book of the sea ever written. It moves awe in the soul'. He had read the incomplete British version. One scours the pages of the two first editions for revelatory differences, but although some thirty-five expurgated passages are restored to the American version there's nothing to snag the scholar's twitchy attention. What interests me, and what I hope will interest you, is the hyphen in the title and its absence in the text.

What's happening there?

Confusion began before the publication of the first British edition and originates in an undated letter, quoted by G. Thomas Tanselle in his introduction to the Library of America edition of *Moby-Dick*, from Melville's brother Allan to the London publisher, Richard Bentley:

> Since sending proofs of my brothers [*sic*] new work [. . .] he has determined upon a new title & dedication – Enclosed you have proof of both – It is thought here that the new title will be a better selling title.

The 'enclosed' were the belated dedication to Nathaniel Hawthorne and the new title, in which Allan, erratically literate, inserted a hyphen by mistake and without his brother's knowledge. Allan's letter arrived in time for Bentley to include the Hawthorne dedication; but it was presumably too late to change the first edition title from THE WHALE, which appears twice in each of the three Bentley volumes and had been used consistently in pre-publication advertising. Only 500 three-volume sets were published and they did not sell well. On the strength of the title and the first fifty pages, prospective buyers might well have mistaken the three volumes as a cetacean *vade mecum*, a guide to the whaling industry, so the unadopted 'better selling title' might have been a belated attempt to brand the book unambiguously as a work of fiction.

Melville's previous books, in common

with many mid-19th-century American novels, all had two-part titles: *Typee: A Peep at Polynesian Life* (1846); *Omoo: A Narrative of Adventures in the South Seas* (1847); *Mardi: And a Voyage Thither* and *Redburn: His First Voyage* (both 1849). The novel immediately preceding *Moby-Dick* was the lavishly-hyphenated *White-Jacket; or, The World in a Man-of-War* (1850).

No manuscript of *Moby-Dick* is known to exist and we cannot be sure what the author had in mind. Melville's many publishers and commentators seem to share a casual indifference to the titular hyphen that, more often than not, results in references to 'Melville's Moby Dick', or (almost as bad) the italicised 'Melville's *Moby Dick*'. Copies of the single-volume American first edition are quite rare – 3,000 were printed and sold slowly, many being destroyed in a warehouse fire. A 'very good' copy is currently advertised online for over $40,000, and the vendor scrupulously includes the title hyphen because for scholars, academics, bibliophiles, booksellers and pedants *Moby-Dick* is the correct (if inconsistently employed) way to write the title, or at least part of the title, of the first American edition of the novel in which Moby Dick is the blubbery and unhyphenated protagonist.

Moby Dick's hyphen is under threat in today's electronic versions; but not only the hyphen. Crucially important aspects of layout are also endangered – numbered pagination, the indentation of new paragraphs, margins, justification, the use of italics, footnotes and almost all the long-established apparatus that (to recycle the Anthony Burgess acronym) makes BOOK a 'Box Of Organised Knowledge'. My Kindle doesn't distinguish between hyphens and dashes, but hyphens still have their place in the typesetter's toolbox, along with the various kinds of dash that serve either to bond together or keep apart. My ebook version of *Moby-Dick* also omits the notorious rogue hyphen that appears in the British first edition. As Melville scholars know, it's on page 609 in Chapter 133, 'The Chase – First Day':

Accordingly, the boats now made for her, and were soon swayed up to their cranes – the two parts of the wrecked boat having been previously secured by her – and then hoisting everything to her side, and stacking her canvas high up, and sideways outstretching it with stunsails, like the double-jointed wings of an albatross; the Pequod bore down in the leeward wake of Moby-Dick.

In that first edition the first half of the whale's name comes at a line break and this may have prompted a zealous typographer to add the hyphen, although its use here implies a creature elsewhere going by the single name of Mobydick, or MobyDick, the cetacean equivalent of Bono and Beyoncé. A printer's error? Or is that first sighting an early example of the conscious intertextual self-referencing beloved of postmodernist academics and the bane of the common reader? My money's on a typo.

Why Moby Dick anyway? What, as one wag put it, is a 'Moby'? The name was not entirely Melville's invention but sourced in an article about the real-life capture of a notoriously violent creature called Mocha Dick, near the Pacific island of that name. The American author and explorer Jeremiah N. Reynolds published a lively account of the incident as *Mocha Dick: Or The White Whale of the Pacific: A Leaf from a Manuscript Journal* in the May 1839 issue of New York's *The Knickerbocker* magazine. We know that Melville obtained a copy before starting work on his novel and clearly had Reynolds's title in mind when it came to naming his own *magnum opus*. 'Moby' has since acquired an independent lexical value as the first part of the name of the whale, and the first part of a version of the the title of the novel in which the whale appears *and nothing else*, unless one includes the musician Richard Melville Hall, who performs under the stage-name of Moby. (Herman was his great-great-great-grand-uncle, which is worth mentioning, if only for its syncopating hyphen-chain.)

Described by Reynolds as 'an old bull whale, of prodigious size and strength', Mocha Dick was also, whether through age or some natural condition, 'as white as wool'. Melville took his cue for the name from the article, discarding the Mocha but retaining the Dick, which seems to have been a whaler's random choice selected from the anonymous triumvirate Tom, Dick and Harry. Moby-Tom and Moby-Harry are both non-starters and 'dick' didn't come into use as a slang term for the male member until the late 19th century. (Whether the phallic euphemism derived indirectly from Melville is not an hypothesis under consideration here). A plausible phonetic link to the Möbius Strip turns out to be another red herring, as this was discovered seven years after the novel was published. How Mocha became Moby is anyone's guess and much ingenious speculation surrounds the transformation, none of it entirely convincing. Can we suppose Moby is a fictional island providing Melville with a physical feature after which an equally fictional whale could be named?

Mocha has an afterlife in your local coffee shop, which is statistically likely to be named after the Pequod's chief mate. From its beginnings in 1971 as a single store (originally to have been named Pequod) there are now 20,500 Starbucks outlets worldwide and the Melville legacy features, dimly, in the twin-tailed mermaid logo and on their corporate website: 'The name, inspired by Moby Dick [*sic*], evoked the romance of the high seas and the seafaring tradition of the early coffee traders.' Coffee seems to have replaced whaling in what appears to be a corporate revisionist take on Moby Dick and *Moby-Dick*. There's more: 'Our mission [is] to inspire and nurture the human spirit – one person, one cup, and one neighbourhood at a time.'

But that's a mission *statement*, not a mission. Ahab has a mission, if a mission is defined as an all-consuming sense of purpose, of personal destiny, and that mission is to kill Moby Dick – one whale, one lance, and one demented monologue at a time. Ahab is a wonderful lunatic, the most exemplary monomaniac in all American literature and, unlike his literary peers Don Quixote and Falstaff, he entirely lacks innocence or charm and is undistorted by self-knowledge. Prompted by an earlier disastrous encounter into becoming the white whale's nemesis, Ahab is a hero only by default, defined by intransigence, a self-serving single-mindedness and an unslakable thirst for vengeance. He's part Long John Silver, part Flying Dutchman, part Biblical monarch (and there may be a phonetic link here – the Hebrew king Ahab's father conquered the land of *Moab*).

Unlike Moby Dick, Ahab's vessel the *Pequod*, that 'fading phantom' with its crew of 'mongrel renegades, and castaways, and cannibals', does have an etymological origin, if an obscure one. Two other fictional (and hyphenated) Nantucket ships are preparing for a three-year trip when Ishmael fetches up in Nantucket – the *Devil-Dam* and the *Tit-bit*. Melville – via Ishmael – tells us the ship to which he signs on is named after the Native American Pequot tribe, and this was a deliberately ominous choice. Although the Pequot people have remarkably survived to this day they represented for the author an image of loss and annihilation – a 1910 census listed just 66 survivors but they were, for Melville/Ishmael, 'as extinct as the ancient Medes'. The *Pequod* is a ship of death, encrusted with scrimshaw, bound on a one-way necronautical odyssey.

Nothing connects the word Moby to the world except for its use by Melville. 'Moby' is an enormous word, a monstrous noun (or possibly adjective) that, despite its vastness, means nothing at all. It has – perhaps surprisingly – never developed an independent usage as an intensifier suggesting size or significance or power, like the tiresomely ubiquitous 'awesome'. Moby Dick's name really *is* awesome, suggesting tremendous physical mass, the incarnation of all whalekind. The hyphen might fancifully be seen as a way of rendering the natural into the cultural, a critical hook for hauling the carcass of meaning onto the slipway of interpretation. *Moby-Dick* is a literary artefact, while Moby Dick is a symbol-laden abstraction plainly drawn from nature, but greater than nature, an all-encompassing metaphor.

In terms of plot *Moby-Dick* consists almost entirely of a postponed denouement contained in the final two chapters. Before that we are given an exhaustive account of the so-called 'fishery', an extended and minutely detailed description of the business of whaling. This 'documentary footage' is transformed by Melville's quite astonishing powers of description and analysis into visionary reportage. Any work of art is functional (operating on the level of its own discourse) and metaphorical. *Moby-Dick* functionally involves whales, and the hunting and slaughter of whales, on this level doing for the *Pequod*, and the now-defunct industry it serves, what Joyce does for Dublin in *Ulysses*. On the metaphorical level, W. H. Auden, in the *The Enchafèd Flood* (1950), claimed that the whole of *Moby-Dick* is 'an elaborate synecdoche' in which whale fishing becomes an image of all our lives, teeming with parable and multiple symbolic correspondences. Auden – or his editors – regularly confuses the title with the creature, but that doesn't detract from the claim that the novel's universality accounts for its cultural longevity.

Almost every chapter of *Moby-Dick* begins with a precise, even pedantic, description of some aspect of whaling, and in almost every chapter the objective documentary language gradually rises to elaborate abstraction or a sometimes hysterical address to the reader, to all humanity, to the imminent divine. This is a maximalist fiction – one that adds to the world rather than subtracts from it – and Melville is a virtuoso maximalist. The celebrated episode in which different crew members offer elaborate and contradictory interpretations of the gold doubloon nailed by Ahab to the *Pequod*'s mast anticipates the modernist deployment of multiple and unreliable narrators and supports the view that the novel, like the whale itself, is a *tabula rasa*, a blank upon which meaning can be inscribed or inferred. Meaning, however, is unstable and contingent.

The choice of the white whale's name seems to have been a late decision. In Chapter 45 Melville lists four candidate leviathans who never make it to the final cut – Timor Jack, New Zealand Tom, Morquan and Don Miguel – none of which has the same aural resonance as Ahab's nemesis, although Jack and Tom may be first cousins to Dick. Morquan? Too weird. Don Miguel? Too Cervantean. One cannot easily conceive of novels entitled *Timor-Jack*, *New Zealand-Tom* or *Don-Miguel*. Moby trails no meaning but is, quite literally, a floating signifier. Just as there are alternative, unexplored whale stories implied by the hypothetical encounters between the three whaling ships and the four short-listed candidates, there is also an alternative Ahab in the shape of Captain Boomer, skipper of the English whaler *Samuel Enderby*. Boomer has lost an arm in an earlier encounter with Moby Dick, and now sports an ivory prosthetic shaped like a mallet. The two maimed captains click their artificial limbs together by way of greeting and settle down, in one of the typically rich and meandering digressions that replace a plot, for Boomer's jocular account of his mutilation. Boomer is cheerful, loquacious and fond of his crew, whom he treats with bantering affection. He is dully human, and humane, unlike Ahab. That the latter is a Quaker – like the *Pequod*'s owners and most of the Nantucket whaling community – suggests a pacific inclination that sits oddly with his scorched, obsessive and murderous nature, and his astonishing final onslaught: '[F]rom hell's heart I stab at thee; for hate's sake I spit my last breath at thee.'

Moby Dick appears by name in just three of the novel's 135 chapters. When first sighted (in Chapter 133) there is a flurry of nominal repetitions – or invocations – accompanied by the traditional fishery cry of 'There she blows', which may make us pause as Moby Dick is elsewhere unambiguously male, a bull sperm whale of prodigious size and power and cunning. There are other distinct characteristics – the skewed or scrolled jawbone, the oddly wrinkled brow, the scarred hide, the embedded fishing tackle, and above all the colour, or lack of it, incarnated in the snow-white hump.

Why should a *white* whale exercise such a profound and lasting purchase on our imagination? Melville's mesmerisingly strange chapter 'On the Whiteness of the Whale' has been the subject of much scholarly analysis and debate. Spectral and ineffable yet always substantial, it is above all the meaninglessness of such a natural anomaly, a surrealist confluence of tone and form without rhyme or reason, that most troubles our dreams. Moby Dick is an elusive creature that, when visible, is wholly, sensationally, unambiguously *visible* – not just any white whale, but *the* white whale. Melville, ranging erratically over the phenomenon of whiteness in nature and culture, unsettlingly equates it not with purity but with the opposite of everything, with oblivion, the 'pallor of the dead'. Just as whiteness is both the sum of all colours and a lack of colour, Moby Dick is simultaneously a mass of meanings and the negation of meaning – an overwhelming accumulation of significance that adds up to everything and nothing at all. We can all of us read *Moby-Dick*, but reading Moby Dick is another matter, because Moby Dick is

a symbol for everything. An ocean of rhetorical elaboration surrounds the whale, with meaning sucked in and expelled like air from a blow-hole, and this instability is reflected perfectly in Melville's blend of documentary precision and pervasive metaphysical dread. The first chapter is, appropriately and portentously, entitled 'Loomings'.

'The sperm whale's unique body is unlikely to be confused with any other species,' says the Wikipedia entry with admirable understatement, but Melville insists that the whale has no body at all, consisting as it does purely of a head and a tail with no intermediate abdomen. This is followed by the author's deeply unsettling observation that the whale has a head but no face. A prodigious mass of meat and muscle, *Physeter macrocephalus* offers no concession to human understanding: the tiny eyes, the near-invisible ears, the cavernous maw – all confirm rather than vitiate the creature's absolute strangeness and inscrutability, in a way that curiously anticipates a spine-chilling moment in G. K. Chesterton's 1908 novel *The Man Who was Thursday:*

> The large face [. . .] grew larger and larger; and Syme was gripped with a fear that when he was quite close the face would be too big to be possible, and that he would scream aloud.

Moby Dick, with or without a face, is too big to be possible. Unknowable, practically unimaginable, the white whale makes our thoughts small, dwarfed both by its uncanny absence and its meticulously realised presence. It's unclear whether Moby Dick survives the final catastrophe – freshly wounded and with his strange cargo of Ahab's entangled corpse, he disappears, leaving Ishmael to float away on Queequeg's empty coffin. Eventually rescued, the narrator fills a role dating back to Anglo-Saxon poetry and the 'ubi sunt' motif – that of a lone figure who lives to tell the tale of those he left behind, a not-so ancient mariner, chronically eloquent and with a leftover life to fill.

We know, up to a point, what a whale is, but what is it for? This is made vividly clear in Melville's descriptions of the process of slaughter, dismemberment and rendering down into oil, the hellishly messy and hazardous business that is the whaling-ship's *raison d'être*. We are spared no detail, from the stomach-turning retrieval of aromatic ambergris buried deep in the head to the feeding-frenzy of sharks gorging on the slung corpse. No creature has ever been so elaborately, intimately anatomised: the Brobdingnagian internal cavities, the hefty organs, the milky spermaceti, the thick layers of flensed flesh, the slicks of black blood, the unctuous oils and the textured offal of white-horse, plum-pudding, slobgollion and gurry.

From fleshy offal to clean-cut technology. 'Mobi' is a top-end internet domain name (prosaically derived from the adjective mobile), and this brings us back to the way things are currently heading. In our digital age the hyphen is going the way of the semi-colon; it is entirely missing from the title of my electronic version of *Moby-Dick*, which is available on Kindle as Moby Dick: or, the White Whale. (Kindle doesn't stretch to italics.) That comma is not uncommon (as we have seen in the case of Melville's earlier *White-Jacket*), and is as well established as the hyphen, but that vampire's puncture of a colon came as a shock. Then it struck me – Kindle have actually got this right! This is surely closest to the form of the title that Melville intended all along, before his brother's letter confused things. Picture it in publisher's caps, the hyphen and colon quietly removed, as **MOBY DICK or THE WHITE WHALE**. Doesn't that look right to you? The harpoon-hyphen removed, the alternative title enhanced (with its satisfying and memorable 'Wh-Wh' alliteration), the whole thing bold and balanced, holding in perfect equilibrium the functional and metaphorical elements of the novel.

I have just re-read 70 per cent of *Moby-Dick* on my fourth generation Amazon Kindle, whose factory setting employs the PMN Caecilia font, a slab-serif typeface which is quite easy on the eye and without the tiny fish-hooks of serif font that would make light skimming a trial. Around twenty lines per screen page (on my basic model) means plenty of right-hand clicking. The benefits of ebooks are self-evident, and there are certain to be new improved models on the market before you finish reading this paragraph. But self-evident benefits aside I dislike the tiresome business of clicking from page to page, of being unable to flick back to an earlier passage or to riffle absent-mindedly. *Moby-Dick* is a novel that demands riffling.

Kindle still has some firmware bugs uncorrected and does not hyphenate. Or, to be precise, the software can but the hardware can't, so it is not unusual to see very loosely set lines which sometimes fail to reach the right-hand margin, creating what's called a 'jagged right', a raggedy appearance diligently avoided by traditional typographers, often by breaking multisyllabic words with a hyphen. Surely this can be fixed. Would such an improvement secure a market lead for the makers? As new brands enter the market – faster, cheaper, better – I suppose we can expect to see improvements all round. Providing, that is, that some literate head of design has a clear idea of how books should look – font, margins, indentation, emspacing and so on.

Against these seismic changes in reading habits my worries about a single hyphen may seem of small account. Yet it strikes me that the ebook industry of the 21st century is a form of gung-ho exploitation not unlike Nantucket whaling in the nineteenth. Novels – bulky, cumbersome, slow-moving, rich in content and wholly exploitable – are, like whales, pursued, captured, radically commodified and made palatable to the consumer. In the process of becoming a flat grey slab the original entity loses its physical integrity, is deprived of texture, of life. The first-time reader of *Moby-Dick* in an electronic format will have access to a reasonably reliable text but may never realise the way the short chapters alternate between narrative and analysis, between Ahab's maniac quest and Melville's own reflections. This great, unwieldy novel, electronically filleted and efficiently packaged for today's hyperkinetic lifestyles, can be dipped into over a mocha frappuccino, but still has a looming cultural presence that transcends its format. I wonder if the same can be said for the Adelaide University ebook version of *Finnegans Wake* which I have recently downloaded and which, in its deliberately unpaginated scroll-like format, may come closer to what Joyce intended than any print version has yet done.

Moby Dick surfaces briefly from the murky lexical depths of the *Wake* as the 'groot hwide Whalefisk' pursued by the harpooner 'queckqueck'. Joyce's last book, a behemoth to match Moby Dick and *Moby-Dick*, also suffers at the hands of careless punctuators. There is never an apostrophe in *Finnegans Wake* but there is always one in 'Finnegan's Wake', the Irish ballad of the 1850s composed around the time Melville was writing *Moby-Dick*. *Finnegans Wake* is a book, of sorts. 'Finnegan's Wake' is not a book at all, and never was, but this is where we came in. Samuel Beckett, writing in defence of Joyce's bewildering masterpiece said: 'His writing is not about something; it is that something itself.' Herman Melville's writing, on the other hand, *is* about something. *Moby-Dick* is a book about Moby Dick, and Moby Dick is everything.

JACK ROBINSON
The Disguise

In June 1819 Henri Beyle – aka Stendhal, the most enduring of his many alternative names – put on an oversize overcoat and green glasses and travelled from Milan to Volterra, where the woman he loved had gone to visit her children. He was thirty-six; he had written no novels, yet, but had published books on music and painting and the cities of Italy, making liberal use of material by other authors, and he had met Mathilde Dembowski in Milan the previous year. Dembowski was aged twenty-nine and separated from the man she had married at seventeen.

'For months I followed strangers on the street . . .' In January 1980 the French artist and writer Sophie Calle followed a man in Paris, lost him after a few minutes, then saw him again by chance that evening at a gallery opening, where he told her he was soon to travel to Venice. She followed him there, taking a suitcase in which she had packed 'a blond, bobbed wig; hats; veils; gloves; sunglasses'. In her account of, quite literally, the following days, she names the man as 'Henri B'.

In the summer of 2014 a woman – call her Metilde, or M – is staying with her two children in an Italian holiday resort, and a man, Beyle, steps off the ferry in thick-lensed sunglasses and an overcoat like those worn by SS officers in war films. Also involved – probably no more than a walk-on role, but this could change – is a man from Senegal who sells sunglasses on the beach; his name is John. M doubts this: it's just part of his sales patter, she thinks; he will be Jean for the French, Jan for the Dutch. Or his real name is so hard to pronounce for anyone not African that he has settled on John at random, a name that he's heard called out or read in a book. Or he was raised in a mission school and assigned his name by some misguided priest – but surely that hasn't happened for some time, not within the lifetime of this John, who she reckons to be aged twenty at most? She will ask him.

Of course Mathilde Dembowski saw through Beyle's disguise. It was joke-shop stuff, not even skin-deep. If you want to pass yourself off as a green-grocer, knowing how to weigh things and add up might help; if you put on a Church of England dog collar, you should have at least read the Prayer Book. Actors, fugitives, con-men and spies know this; as do those whose religious beliefs or sexual preferences have condemned them to lead undercover lives; as do people applying for jobs in which they've had no experience. But Beyle was seeking not to be *someone else* but anonymity, a harder thing; or rather, he was seeking to be there but not have his thereness noticed, like an author with the kind of style that gets called transparent. The man who had sold him his coat swore it was an invisibility coat. It was second-hand, so there were some rips and stains, some of the invisibility had worn off.

In 1819 Beyle retreated to Milan, chastised, and wrote a humdrum letter of apology: 'it occurred to me that by wearing green spectacles and changing my coat I could quite well spend two or three days at Volterra, going out only at night and without being recognised by you' (letter to Dembowski dated 11 June). When Mathilde returned to Milan she refused Beyle as a lover but allowed him to visit her once every two weeks. In 1820 Beyle completed the first draft of *De l'Amour* and sent it to France, where it was lost in the post for over a year.

In 2014 Beyle stays on in the Italian resort for some days. The weather is not good but he has never been one for the beach. He visits churches and the local museum. He buys postcards and wonders who to send them to. He observes couples, not all of them Japanese, taking photographs of each other in front of a fountain or a gateway or a railing overlooking a view of distant hills; some of these couples approach Beyle and offer a little mime, and he takes their camera and they pose together, holding their smiles very steady – as if the conventions of being photographed established 150 years ago, when exposure times were long, still apply; or, more likely, because we owe it to ourselves to enter the future looking at our best: see, grandchildren, we were happy, we were in love – and he presses a tiny button. *Then* they relax, and their faces light up. He invites M to dinner.

She is not conciliatory. She accuses Beyle of an 'invasion of privacy' and then, annoyed with Beyle, or me, for saddling her with such terrible lines, tells Beyle that he is no better than a stalker, and his use of her as an object on which to project his desires is basically a pornographic use. She tells him to go, *now*; she knows the ferry doesn't sail until late the next day but there must be flights from the airport, they're not stuck in the nineteenth century. Beyle says the twentieth would be worse. They are in the dining room of Beyle's hotel, and he recommends the octopus cooked in a kind of chilli sauce. 'Maybe we should just fuck,' M suggests, as if reading aloud from the menu, trying out the sound of the words – 'We're already in a hotel. You have a room. The lift is just over there' – and then 'you could get on with the rest of your life, and me too'. But that wouldn't work because 'what you're really in love with is your suffering. You despise the kind of love you call mannered but you thrive on it. Every glance, every blush, you analyse, explain, classify . . . It's geekish. Voyeuristic. Adolescent.' Beyle tries to defend himself by saying porn maybe, but quality porn, *literary* porn, and even if she isn't interested in him as a lover she can't help but be interested in his being a writer – they had met at a literary salon, after all – but line by line the conversation just peters out, and so did my story. 'Everything we've said has been said by everyone else in this room,' M remarks. Beyle points out that the dining room is now empty. But it isn't: there's a waitress and two waiters. They don't count, Beyle says; they are bored, they just want to clock off and go to bed. I'll get the bill.

Beyle and waiters/waitresses have history. In *Travels in the South of France* he rants about the waiters of Marseilles, Lyons and Bordeaux; he carries his tea leaves with him and asks just for hot water, and 'the reader will have perhaps noticed my habit of measuring the degree of civilisation by the degree of hot water I am served'. Impossible to know, of course, whether the waiters were in fact just toying with this stranger from out of town, or taking revenge for his grumpiness. Waitresses, on the other hand: 'The young lady leant over the counter, and had thus an opportunity of displaying a superb figure. Julien noticed it. *All his ideas changed.* The pretty young lady had just placed before him a cup, some sugar, and a little roll.' (*Le Rouge et le Noir*; my italics.) Jhumpa Lahiri, in an interview published in *Granta*, wanting to learn about Mavis Gallant's writing habits when she first arrived in Paris, asked if she had ever worked in cafés. No, no, Gallant replied, she was never a waitress.

On her second day in Venice Sophie Calle, wearing her blond wig, is herself followed by an unknown man. On her fourth day she discovers where Henri B is staying. On her seventh day, after spending much of the two previous days loitering outside B's hotel while trying to appear inconspicuous, she finally sees him; for an hour she follows B and his female companion through a maze of streets and alleys, taking photographs of them along the way, including one of B himself taking a photograph. In the evening she follows him again, until he and the woman go into an antique shop and and don't come out; after two hours of waiting in the cold outside (it's February), Calle asks a passing stranger to enter the shop and report back on what is happening inside; her reason, she explains, is that she is in love with the man ('only love seems admissable'). On the eighth day she follows B again, another meander through the winding streets until, becoming aware of her presence, he turns and recognises her: 'Your eyes, I recognise your eyes; that's what you should have hidden.' They walk and take a vaporetto together, making desultory conversation. ('What did I imagine? That he was going to take me with him, to challenge me, to use me? Henri B did nothing. I discovered nothing. A banal ending to this banal story.') They separate. Calle goes to the carnival, dances, spends the night on a bench with a harlequin. On the ninth and tenth days she watches B's hotel entrance from the window of an upper room in a nearby house. She learns the reasons for B's trip to Venice: to scout locations for a film he is planning and to take photographs 'for a book by C, the English writer'. On the eleventh day she learns that B and his partner will be returning to Paris by train that night; she finds another train, via Bologna, that will arrive in Paris five minutes before B's train. The following morning, in Paris, she photographs B 'one last time as he passes through the station gate'.

I kept wanting to push my Beyle/Metilde story back from now, to frame the whole episode in a particular period of gender politics that would reflect both back (to 1819) and forward (to the time of my writing). Back to the 1970s, when I was in my twenties, as Mathilde was in 1819, and the children in the tale wouldn't be held hostage by their iPhones; back further, to the 1950s, before colour TV, when the story would naturally be in black and white. Beyle himself was constantly pushing forward the date at which he had any hope of being read: 1880, 1900, 1935 . . . He *distrusted* the present. In *Travels in the South of France* he lists some prices ('excellent room at the Hôtel Casset, 1 franc; table d'hôte dinner plentiful but table companions unmannerly, 2.50 francs'), begs the reader's forgiveness but suggests this may be of value 'in 1880, if, however, this rubbish is still in existence then'. Writing to Prosper Mérimée on the subject of impotence, he explained that in his customary way of writing, which he termed 'the black-on-white style' ('le genre noir sur du blanc'), honest depictions of sex were not possible, and promised he would be more explicit 'in 2826, if civilisation continues and I return to the rue Duphot'. There are days when Beyle and I pass each other in the street, unawares, walking in opposite directions.

If Beyle hadn't wanted to sleep with M, and M not wanted to sleep with him, they could have had a perfectly civilised conversation in the hotel dining room, and in another failed draft of my story they drink a second bottle of wine and try for this. M knows that Beyle is writing a book and that it's not a novel, more a kind of essay, and she approves. People don't want stories, she says: 'They want to be told how to live their lives, they want *advice*.' The author as agony aunt. The novel is *passé*; it's been killed by the internet, which has wrecked our attention spans. I want to disagree, and draw up a chair at the table with M and Beyle. I talk about my friend who opens a novel at a random page and reads for however long he cares to read, and ditto when he picks up the book again later, and this dipping in and out seems to me no less valid than reading *in a straight line*. M laughs: it's how most people read the *LRB*, she says, so buy him a subscription and he won't have even have to bother with novels. Well, yes – here the one remaining waiter aproaches and offers me a menu: thank you but no: I'm just stopping by, I'm not staying – but if we think of writing as a matter of *sentences*, then even if the narrative tra-la is just scaffolding it's still *story* that delivers the best ones. Beyle asks if I've read Flaubert's letter to Louise Colet in which he spoke of writing 'a book about nothing, a book . . . held aloft by the internal force of its style, as the earth stays aloft on its own'. He seems a little pleased with himself for remembering that quote; I think he is tiring, has reached his limit. I myself would now like a glass of wine, but our waiter has got bored with our bookish talk and disappeared. I take a bottle from the rack behind the bar and look for a corkscrew: this is *my* story, after all, and I'm thirsty. M, meanwhile, who once worked for a few months as an intern in the marketing department of a trade publisher, is still enthusiastic about Beyle's new book having some instructional point. Though she *is* very pretty, I'm beginning to go off her: at heart she's just another puritan, one of the tribe that insists that literature is good for you. She disapproves of skipping; she believes you should always finish a book, even though we all know that endings are often the weakest bit. Beyle's book, M speculates – and though she suspects it is about love, which is what Beyle goes on about, she has no intention of interfering, except to demand that she herself be kept out if it – a condition that Beyle agreed to: *De l'Amour*, though taking its whole charge from his relationship with Mathilde Dembowski, contains no mention of her – Beyle's book, to give this sentence back its subject, might get onto the reading lists for students at colleges, might even become a *set book*, in which case would become rich. And thereafter he'd be able to have any woman he wants, or so the story goes, but I doubt that. Beyle shrugs. By his own count, seventeen copies of *De l'Amour* were sold in its first eleven years. His first novel, *Armance*, published in 1827, whose main character suffers from impotence, fared no better.

'There is nothing ridiculous about dying in the street, provided one does not do it on purpose' – Beyle, in a letter written a year before he collapsed in the street in Paris in 1842 and died a few hours later. (A note in his pocket identified him as 'Arrigo Beyle, Milanese'; three newspaper reports of his death spelled his name wrong, a book tells me, and even then I don't know *which* name.) I think of Vallejo's poem – 'I will die in Paris, on a rainy day, on a day I can already remember . . .' – and of the sequence of photographs of a man dying in a Paris street taken by Brassaï from the window of an upper room overlooking the scene. Street photography used to be about capturing a chance moment; now, Jeff Wall *re-stages* street scenes, using actors.

To furnish the backstory of a character he named Maria in his 1992 novel *Leviathan*, Paul Auster used a number of Sophie Calle's projects – including her following of Henri B in Venice; a variant of this, in which she herself is followed by a private detective; and working for a month in a Paris night-club as a stripper (but again wearing a blond wig, 'in case my grandparents, who lived in the neighbourhood, should happen to pass by'; Brassaï, in his photographs taken in Paris brothels in the 1920s, had friends substitute for the camera-shy real clients, who worried about their wives as Calle worried about her grandparents). In response, Calle performed a number of additional projects that Auster invented for his fictional character. Up to a point I find this interesting, and after that point no less annoying than Mathilde Dembowski found Henri Beyle's overcoat and green glasses. Smoke and mirrors.

On and off, I've been following Henri B for two decades without getting any closer (or knowing what I'd do if I did get close). A few times I've tried reading him in French and given up. He wrote at a speed – the whole of *La Chartreuse de Parme* in fifty-three days – I find dizzying. His name, the one he's best known by and the one I'm not even confident in pronouncing right, is an anagram of Shetland. The name of the young prostitute in London who promised that if he'd take her with him to France she would cost him nothing, she would eat only apples, was Miss Appleby. He was short and overweight and after his hair fell out when he was young he wore a toupee. Paris, when he first arrived there from the provinces, was a disappointment: there were no mountains, and the trees were pruned. He bungled things: as a vice-consul in Italy, he sent a letter in code and included the key to the code in the same envelope. He barked up wrong trees, pruned or not. He once went to Newcastle. He started more books than he finished. In his own attempt to replay in writing the Volterra episode, which was also his first attempt at fiction – Mathilde is re-named Bianca, the would-be lover is Poloski, and between them there's a lesbian duchess – he got no further than the first chapter.

Anthony Barnett at Allardyce Book

Anthony Barnett is like no other poet of his generation, yet both his elliptical lyrics and his work in longer spans should be part of the current consensus of what constitutes our modern poetry.   - Tony Frazer, Shearsman Books

As poet and publisher for the past forty-five years Anthony Barnett has ploughed a solitary furrow, unerringly straight and hauntingly evocative across the field of English poetry. That furrow owes little to a notion of landscape or cityscape as it is conceived within the confines of much British poetry over the last half-century . . . Anthony Barnett remains one of the most important translators of poetry into English that we have in this country and in his lecture at Meiji University in 2002, titled InExperience and UnCommon Sense in Translation, we can see why that should be.   - Ian Brinton, Poetry Review

He appears very un-English in his writing—as Englishness tends currently to be thought of, that is—and this is one important reason why he has not had the recognition he deserves. But Barnett is very much an English poet, and his best poetry is wholly opposed to the slack and ingratiating verse that has been dominating British letters for too long; Barnett himself has made no secret of his contempt for its practitioners and its busy facilitators, the mostly mediocre functionaries of literature who have bought into the easy prejudices of the age—this, too, has helped to ensure his neglect. . . . Another reason for this neglect is that he is his own publisher—as well as the publisher, in beautiful editions, of work by, among others, J. H. Prynne, Veronica Forrest-Thomson, Andrew Crozier and Douglas Oliver. The Allardyce, Barnett imprint has been and remains a very important one. . . . In an often lonely and difficult career, Barnett has kept open roads that too many British poets have chosen to ignore or to seek to close, if, indeed, they have even been aware of them. His best work is bracing and challenging and deserves to be recognised for the major achievement it is. The publication of these two volumes together is a very important literary event, and everybody who has any interest at all in poetry should read them. - Timothy Harris, PN Review

The poetry resists the "big world" into which it is sent out, not only the big world of the poetry business. It views that world as decadent, or an illusion, and seeks to render it as an obedient thing in which the self's needs can be met—an earthly paradise. It hammers on the door of this place, it sings against the barrier to it. Celan too projected an unreachable verbal paradise as the echo of a mystic tongue. The writing is oppositional, in the guise of a self demanding its due, but offers unsullied guarantees of earthly reality and a particular form of elegance in exchange—that is the contract with the reader. It can never be the only way. Explicitly expansive modes of poetry are needed if the art is to maintain a position in modernity, but the absence of exceptions such as Barnett's would be a very sad loss. - Peter Riley, Fortnightly Review

Anthony Barnett has also worked as a percussionist, notably with John Tchicai, and such as Derek Bailey, Don Cherry, Leo Smith. His research into the history of jazz violin has been featured in The Wall Street Journal, The Strad *and* Grove

Poems &
poetry and prose 1968–2012, 978-0-907954-46-0, 658pp, £48, or £36 with Translations

Translations
Akutagawa, Albiach, Delahaye, Des Forêts, Giroux, Lagerkvist, Vesaas, Zanzotto and others, 978-0-907954-47-7, 342pp, £36, or £25 with Poems &, both in assoc. Tears in the Fence

Listening for Henry Crowder
A Monograph on His Almost Lost Music, with cd
featuring a 1930 Paris recording by Crowder of a blues by Nancy Cunard and a new recording of his setting to a poem by Samuel Beckett sung by Allan Harris, 978-0-907954-36-1, 128pp, £36

InExperience and UnCommon Sense in Translation
with Some Reference to Umberto Eco's Experiences in Translation *with appendix*
Thinking About Translation, 978-0-907954-51-4, 32pp, £5, or free with Snow 3 subscription

Snow *lit rev*
prose, poetry, music, art, film, photography, edited by Anthony Barnett and Ian Brinton
NO. I, SPRING 2013, *includes etching by* Gisèle Celan-Lestrange; *letter by* J. H. Prynne *on* Celan
NO. 2, FALL 2013–SPRING 2014, *includes* Anthony Barnett-George Oppen *letters*; Prynne *Shen Zhou* Albiach *posthumous work*; William Fuller; Mandelstam; Ungaretti; Zanzotto *poems*; Zurita
NO 3, SPRING 2015, *includes* Cees Nooteboom-Anthony Barnett *correspondence*; Zanzotto *essay*
visit www.abar.net/snow.pdf *for downloadable content and subscription information*

www.abar.net | Allardyce, Barnett, Publishers | ab@abar.net
07816 788442 | 14 Mount Street · Lewes · East Sussex BN7 1HL | 01273 479393

Contributors

Nina Bogin was born in New York and has lived in France for many years. She is the author of three collections of poetry, most recently *The Lost Hare* (Anvil, 2012); her translation of Agota Kristof's memoir *The Illiterate* was published by CBe in 2013.

Beverley Bie Brahic's poetry collection *White Sheets* (CBe, 2012) was short-listed for the Forward Prize; her translations of poems by Apollinaire, *The Little Auto* (CBe, 2011), won the 2014 Scott Moncrieff Translation Prize; *Unfinished Ode to Mud* (CBe, 2009), her translations of Francis Ponge, was shortlisted for the Popescu Prize. Her translation of Ponge's 'My Creative Method', printed in this issue, first appeared in *Maisonneuve*, Montreal, in 2002; it has been lightly revised.

David Collard is a writer and researcher based in London. He reviews regularly for the *TLS* and blogs at davidjcollard.blogspot.co.uk. His book on Eimear McBride, *About a Girl*, will be published by CBe in 2015.

Will Eaves is the author of four novels and a collection of poetry (*Sound Houses*, Carcanet, 2011). He was Arts Editor of the *Times Literary Supplement* from 1995 to 2011, and now teaches at the University of Warwick. *The Absent Therapist* (CBe, 2014) was shortlisted for the Goldsmiths Prize.

Andrew Elliott lives in London. His books include *Lung Soup* (Blackstaff, 2009) and *Mortality Rate* (CBe, 2013).

Nancy Gaffield was born in the United States and lived in Japan for many years; she currently works as a senior lecturer at the University of Kent. Her first collection of poetry, *Tokaido Road* (CBe, 2011), won the Aldeburgh First

Collection Prize and was shortlisted for the Forward First Collection Prize; an opera derived from *Tokaido Road* premiered in 2014. Her other poetry publications are *Owhere* (Templar, 2012) and *Continental Drift* (Shearsman, 2014).

Agota Kristof (1935–2011) was born in Hungary and became an exile in French-speaking Switzerland in 1956. Working in a factory, she slowly learned the language of her adopted country. Her first novel, *The Notebook* (*Le Grand Cahier*, 1986; reissued by CBe in 2014), gained international recognition; *The Proof* (*La Preuve*, 1988) and *The Third Lie* (*Le Troisième Mensonge*, 1991) – reissued in one volume by CBe in 2015 – complete the trilogy of novels in which she, as an émigré writer, forged wholly distinctive ways to treat the 20th-century European experience of war, occupation and separation. Her stories in this issue, from her book *C'est égal* (2005), are printed by permission of Editions du Seuil.

Elizabeth Mikesch lives in Detroit, Michigan. She is the author of *Niceties: Aural Ardor, Pardon Me* (Calamari, 2014) and the co-founder of (. y .) press, an all-girl publishing project. In addition to writing short stories, she performs contemporary folk arias as Fat Friend.

J. O. Morgan lives in Scotland. His first book, *Natural Mechanical* (CBe, 2009) won the Aldeburgh First Collection Prize and was shortlisted for the Forward First Collection Prize; its sequel, *Long Cuts* (CBe, 2011), was shortlisted for a Scottish Book Award. *At Maldon* (CBe, 2013) was shortlisted for the Saltire Society Poetry Book of the Year award.

D. Nurkse lives in Brooklyn, New York. He has published ten collections of poetry, of which CBe has published two in UK editions: *Voices over Water* (2011; shortlisted for the Forward Prize) and *A Night in Brooklyn* (2013).

Dan O'Brien is a playwright and poet living in Los Angeles. His *War Reporter* (CBe, 2013) won the Fenton Aldeburgh Prize for a first collection of poetry and was shortlisted for the Forward First Collection Prize; his second collection, *Scarsdale*, was published by CBe in 2014. His play *The Body of an American* won the Horton Foote Prize and the inaugural Edward M. Kennedy Prize for Drama, and had its European premiere in London in 2014. For another poem in the ongoing War Reporter series he won the 2014 Troubabour International Poetry Competition.

Francis Ponge (1899–1988) developed an influential form of the prose poem, 'reconstructing the physical nature of the world by means of the impalpable, powder-fine dust of words' (Italo Calvino). He also collaborated with painters including Braque, Dubuffet, Fautrier and Picasso. A bilingual edition of his poems, *Unfinished Ode to Mud*, translated by Beverley Bie Brahic, was published by CBe in 2008.

Jack Robinson (a pen-name of Charles Boyle) is the author of *Recessional* (CBe, 2009) and of *Days and Nights in W12* (CBe, 2011).

Adnan Sarwar served with the Royal Engineers during two tours of Iraq. His 'British Muslim Soldier' won the 2013 Bodley Head/Financial Times Essay Prize. More of his writing is at www.adnansarwar.com.

May-Lan Tan is the author of the story collection *Things to Make and Break* (CBe, 2014), which was shortlisted for the Guardian First Book Award; and of the chapbook *Girly* (Future Tense, 2014). She is a collaborator with Marina Abramovic Institute's *Immaterial*.

Ryan Van Winkle is a poet, live artist, podcaster and critic living in Edinburgh. His poems have appeared in *New Writing Scotland*, *The Prairie Schooner*, *The American Poetry Review*, *AGNI* and *The Australian Book Review*. His second collection is due out in 2015 from Penned in the Margins.